The Shorter
Forms of
Building Contract

The Shorter Forms of Building Contract

Third Edition

HUGH CLAMP
OBE, VRD*, FRIBA, PPLI

OXFORD

BLACKWELL SCIENTIFIC PUBLICATIONS

LONDON EDINBURGH BOSTON

MELBOURNE PARIS BERLIN VIENNA

© 1984, 1988, 1993 by Hugh Clamp

Except
The JCT Agreement for Minor
Building Works, 1980 Edition, January 1992
Revision © RIBA Publications Ltd
Conditions of Contract for Building
Works of a Jobbing Character JA/C 90
© 1990 British Property Federation together
with Association of County Councils,
Association of Metropolitan Authorities and
Association of District Councils.

Blackwell Scientific Publications
Editorial Offices:
Osney Mead, Oxford OX2 0EL
25 John Street, London WC1N 2BL
23 Ainslie Place, Edinburgh EH3 6AJ
238 Main Street, Cambridge,
    Massachusetts 02142, USA
54 University Street, Carlton
    Victoria 3053, Australia

Other Editorial Offices:
Librairie Arnette SA
2, rue Casimir-Delavigne
75006 Paris
France

Blackwell Wissenschafts-Verlag GmbH
Meinekestrasse 4
D-1000 Berlin 15
Germany

Blackwell MZV
Feldgasse 13
A-1238 Wien
Austria

First edition published by Granada
    Publishing 1984
Second edition published by
    BSP Professional Books 1988
Third edition published by Blackwell
    Scientific Publications 1993

Set by DP Photosetting, Aylesbury, Bucks
Printed and bound in Great Britain by
Hartnolls Ltd, Bodmin, Cornwall

DISTRIBUTORS

Marston Book Services Ltd
PO Box 87
Oxford OX2 0DT
(*Orders:* Tel: 0865 791155
        Fax: 0865 791927
        Telex: 837515)

USA
Blackwell Scientific Publications, Inc.
238 Main Street
Cambridge, MA 02142
(*Orders:* Tel: 800 759-6102
            617 225-0401)

Canada
Oxford University Press
70 Wynford Drive
Don Mills
Ontario M3C 1J9
(*Orders:* Tel: 416 441-2941)

Australia
Blackwell Scientific Publications
(Australia) Pty Ltd
54 University Street
Carlton, Victoria 3053
(*Orders:* Tel: 03 347-0300)

British Library
Cataloguing in Publication Data
A Catalogue record for this book is
available from the British Library

ISBN 0-632-03384-3

Library of Congress
Cataloging in Publication Data

Clamp, Hugh.
    The shorter forms of building contract/
    Hugh Clamp. — 3rd ed.
        p.   cm.
    Includes bibliographical references and
    index.
    ISBN 0-632-03384-3
    1. Construction contracts—Great Britain.
2. Construction contracts—Great Britain—
Forms.   I. Title.
KD1641.C53   1993
343.41'07869—dc20
[344.1037869]   92-34010
                                        CIP

Contents

Preface to the third edition

In 1979 sales of the 1968 edition of the JCT Minor Works Form amounted to just over 51,500 copies compared with 67,500 copies of JCT 63. Thirteen years later in 1991, the sales of MW 80 had increased to nearly 72,000 and the sales of JCT 80 and Intermediate Form IFC 84 had fallen to 22,700 and 22,300 respectively, a combined total of 45,000. While this is no doubt indicative of the changed pattern of workload in the building industry, it is also due to the widespread acceptance of MW 80 for use on a variety of projects.

Since this book was first published in 1984, a number of significant changes have occurred. Value added tax was introduced and then the distinction between new work and repair or maintenance was subsequently removed. The Intermediate Form IFC 84 was published, the Building Regulations were revised in 1985 and the Latent Damage Act enacted in 1986.

The third edition of this book takes account of a number of other significant changes. MW 80 has been revised by the deletion of the fair wages clauses and the incorporation of the JCT Arbitration Rules in 1988 covered by the Amendment 5 of July that year. Amendment 6 in April 1989 was issued to take account of the 1989 Finance Act, with further changes to the VAT Rules for construction, and Amendment 7 in July 1991 clarified the definition of 'the Works', and liability of the contractor, sub-contractors and suppliers for defects.

In 1990 the JCT introduced a Standard Form of Contract for Jobbing Work, GC/Works/2 was revised, and the New Engineering Contract was published. The new edition of this book includes all these. Furthermore, two cases involving the MW 80 conditions were considered by the High Court (*Tomkinson* v. *St Michaels PCC* and *Othieno* v. *Cooper*) followed by a further case in 1992 (*Corfield* v. *Grant*), all of which have been incorporated in this present edition.

This book is written from the standpoint of a practitioner and I am grateful to John Parris and the Joint Secretaries of the Joint Contracts Tribunal for their attempts over the years to explain to me the legal aspects. If I have still got them wrong I have only myself to blame. I am also indebted to Julia Burden for all her help, without which this text would be even more indigestible than it is. The Minor Works Agreement reproduced on page 164 is the copyright of RIBA Publications Ltd of Finsbury Mission, Moreland Street, London EC1V 8BB, who also publish the JA/C 90 conditions of contract reproduced on page 184. These are reproduced here with the publisher's permission. No other reproduction is permitted.

Hugh Clamp
January 1993

References

Building Contracts, Donald Keating (Sweet & Maxwell), 5th Edition, 1991

Building Law Reports (Longman), 1976–

Hudson's Building and Engineering Contracts, I.N. Duncan Wallace (Sweet & Maxwell), 10th Edition, 1970

The Standard Form of Building Contract, Derek Walker-Smith (Charles Knight & Co.) 1985–

The Standard Form of Building Contract: JCT 80, John Parris (Collins), 2nd Edition, 1985

A Commentary on the JCT Intermediate Form, Neil F. Jones and David Bergman (BSP Professional Books), 2nd Edition, 1990

A User's Guide to the JCT Arbitration Rules, Neil F. Jones (BSP Professional Books), 1989

"Do you mean that you think you can find out the answer to it?" said the March Hare.

"Exactly so," said Alice.

"Then you should say what you mean," the March Hare went on.

"I do," Alice hastily replied; "at least—at least I mean what I say—that's the same thing, you know."

"Not the same thing a bit!" said the Hatter. "You might just as well say that 'I see what I eat' is the same thing as 'I eat what I see'!"

From *Alice's Adventures in Wonderland*, Lewis Carroll.
Illustration by John Tenniel, published by Macmillan Children's Books, a division of Macmillan Publishers Ltd

Introduction

The advantages of standard contracts

Building contracts are in a category of their own as 'work and materials' contracts. They are not contracts for the sale of goods at common law nor are they subject to the Sales of Goods Act 1979, even though ultimately title in the materials is intended to pass to the building owner, but they are subject to the provisions of the Supply of Goods and Services Act 1982.

To be binding on both parties, there is no legal requirement that building contracts should be in any special form. Agreements are not infrequently made, especially for repairs, by word of mouth. However the result is often that there are disputes subsequently as to what actually was agreed. In addition, to be effective, such simple oral agreements usually have to be augmented by terms implied by the courts, that is, in effect, terms 'written in' because the parties have neglected to agree express terms which cover the situation which has arisen.

Agreements in the form of an exchange of letters may sometimes, but not always, free the parties from disputes about what actually had been agreed but certainly do not exempt them from disputes about the full terms of the contract. The only safe way of commissioning building work by letter is to annex the terms of a standard contract by reference, by the use of such words as 'subject to the terms of the JCT Minor Works Agreement, 1980 edition': see *Modern Buildings* v. *Limmer & Trinidad* (1975). Even then, great care has to be taken to ensure that it is made clear, where there are alternatives (such as those in the Minor Works Agreement in the recitals and in clauses 6.3A and 6.3B regarding insurance), which alternative is being adopted. A contract which has a multitude of alternatives, such as that put forward by the Association of Consultant Architects, cannot safely be annexed by references.

There are also dangers for a building owner who drafts his own contract. To start with, contractors are likely to be suspicious of it and price it accordingly.

But there are also legal objections. By the Unfair Contract Terms Act 1977, some terms may be unforceable and avoided by section 3 where the contractor deals with 'the other's standard form of contract'. But in any event, a court will construe an employer's own contract *contra proferentem;* that is, wherever there is ambiguity in the wording (and there are no contracts without some ambiguities) the meaning most hostile to the employer, and most in favour of the contractor, will be adopted by the courts.

The advantage of a form of building contract agreed and prepared jointly by contractors and employers' representatives is that it will not be subject to the vagaries of the Unfair Contract Terms Act 1977, nor will it be construed *contra proferentem* the employer, or require endorsement by the Office of Fair Trading.

Some courts have held that where a standard contract is drafted by representatives of the industry it is not to be treated as the employer's contract. There is, therefore, every reason why an employer should use a standard form, preferably one drafted collectively by the industry's representative body, the Joint Contracts Tribunal.

It has been said that a contract that does not clearly express the intentions of the parties is worse than no contract at all. Equally if the terms, conditions and obligations of each are not concisely and intelligibly set out problems are inevitable.

'Words,' said Lord Denning, 'are the lawyer's tools of trade. When you have to draw up a will or a contract you have to choose your words well. You have to look into the future – envisage all the contingencies that come to pass – and then use words to provide them. On the words you use your client's future may depend.' (*The Discipline of the Law*, London, 1979)

The meaning of the words, however, depends not only on definitions given in a dictionary, but also on their context within the sentence in which they occur, on any special meaning that has been established for them over the years by accepted usage and on any meaning given to them by legal precedent arising from a judgment given as a result of a dispute in the courts.

Those involved in building contracts frequently turn, therefore, to legal commentaries in the hope that they will there find the true meaning of the words used in the contract explained in a clear and comprehensive fashion.

This book does not aim to be a legal commentary. However, it does aim to amplify the shorter forms of building contract in order to give a better understanding of them and to highlight any practical difficulties.

For in preparing the shorter forms, the draughtsmen have had to resort to shortcuts to achieve their aim of brevity. Welcome as it is, this brevity can produce its own problems.

The main JCT 80 contract has been subjected to criticism for its lack of intelligibility and conciseness. The same cannot be said of the 1980 JCT Form of Agreement for Minor Building Works (MW 80 as it will be termed in this book) for it is generally held to be well thought out and correctly presented, with the obvious virtues of clarity and simplicity.

The range of forms
There are currently six or more different types of contract for procuring buildings in the United Kingdom, ranging from package deal and design and build, at the one end, through lump sum, approximate quantities to cost plus and management contracts at the other. Almost all now have standard forms accepted and used, if not sufficiently well understood, by the building industry in the UK with similar but separate versions for central government, local authorities, the private sector and special versions for use in Scotland. The choice of the most appropriate form for any particular project depends on a variety of factors, such as the time available before the building must be completed and ready for occupation, the time available for the preparation of tender documents, the detailed knowledge of the scope of the work and employers' requirements at the outset, the possibility of variations being required to be incorporated during the progress of the work and the possibility of having to have consultants and specialist sub-contractors chosen and appointed by the employer before the main contract is let. All must be considered and given their respective priorities before the decision as to the type of contract to be used is made. This can best be expressed diagrammatically (see Figure 1).

Public sector JCT contracts
Where the project relies on public sector finance – and in the past a significant proportion had – the requirement that the authorised expenditure be fixed before the contract is let, and for any variations to be accurately priced in accordance with strictly laid down procedures and previously agreed rates, has resulted in the choice of lump sum contracts for the majority of projects. These may or may not have quantities provided by the employer and include the option for the recovery by the contractor of increased costs arising during the progress of the works where the contract period exceeds twelve months.

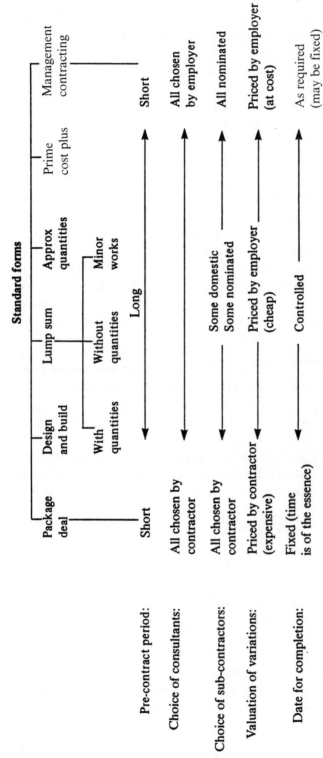

Figure 1

The 1968 Minor Works Contract

The changes of pattern of the work resulted in the Joint Contracts Tribunal (JCT) issuing its first Agreement for Minor Building Works in June 1968 (MW 68). This was initially drafted by George Davies, then Senior Partner of Gleeds, the quantity surveyors, of Nottingham. He achieved what everyone until then considered impossible, a four-page condensed version, of the JCT 63 Standard Form, which at the time ran to thirty-eight pages.

MW 68 was stated in the headnote as being designed for minor building works or maintenance work for which a specification or specification and drawings had been prepared, and where work was to be carried out for an agreed lump sum with an architect or supervising officer appointed on behalf of the employer. The form was said not to be appropriate for works for which bills of quantities had been prepared or for which a schedule of rates was required for valuing possible variations.

Although not actually stated in the headnote to the form, MW 68 was said to be suitable for contracts of a value of no more than £8000. This was the sum above which the National Federation of Building Trades Employers (NFBTE) – now the Building Employers Confederation – had agreed no member would tender without bills of quantities having been prepared by the employer. This agreement had, of course, been cancelled five years earlier after the case of *In re Birmingham Association of Building Trades Employers' Agreement* (1963) when it was held to be contrary to the public interest and a violation of the Restrictive Trade Practices Act 1956.

The Form rapidly gained acceptance and was adopted for a wide variety of projects. At one stage the JCT even produced an adaptation for use on improvement grant works where no architect was involved and the grants were paid direct to the builder. However, this variant was little used and was not reprinted. It lapsed when MW 80 was published.

Amendments to the 1968 version

During the currency of the 1968 version, changed circumstances resulted in substantial amendments becoming necessary.

The introduction of Value Added Tax and the highly ambiguous requirements of the Finance Act 1972 resulted in the addition of a lengthy new clause.

There followed another lengthy amendment, thought necessary as a result of the Finance Act 1975 which provided for tax to be deducted by the employer from payments due to labour-only sub-contractors who did not have a certificate of exemption under the Act.

Similarly, changes became necessary as the result of a highly unsuccessful Counter-Inflation Act and subsequent statutory instruments. By 1976, MW 68 had grown from fifteen clauses on four pages to seventeen on eight pages plus a supplement. As a consequence there was a substantially altered reprint in 1977.

At the same time, no doubt partly due to the change in pattern and size of projects in the industry referred to earlier, there was a growing dissatisfaction with the full 1963 editions of the Standard Form (JCT 63) at least among architects, and a demand arose for a new shorter form suitable for the majority of lump sum building contracts with or without quantities.

As early as January 1972, in a memorandum to the JCT, the Royal Institute of British Architects (RIBA) had listed ten aspects of JCT 63 which it considered required changing to make clearer the intention of the form, eliminate obsolete practices and allow for recognition of new ones. The complete list was as follows:

(1) To change the words 'practically complete' with its colloquial meaning and remove the anomalies in clause 15 on practical completion and in clause 16 on sectional completion.

(2) To require the contractor to give notice when the works were complete and to warrant that they were in conformity with the contract documents.

(3) To redraft clause 30(7) to remove the inequitable effects against the employer.

(4) To separate additional information provided for the contractor more distinctly from variations.

(5) To provide for shop drawings by the contractor to be acknowledged in the contract and to establish procedures for their distribution.

(6) To incorporate the requirement for the provision of a progress schedule by the contractor in the contract conditions to assist in granting extensions to the contract period.

(7) To give the contractor the right of suspending, rather than determining, the works in the event of non-payment of an interim certificate.

(8) To exclude the $2\frac{1}{2}$ per cent discount to nominated sub-contractors from nominated sub-contract tenders.

(9) To define more clearly the responsibilities of nominated sub-contractors and suppliers.

(10) To redraft the whole contract into a more intelligible form and

logical sequence, while not delaying the preparation of a standard form of nominated sub-contract.

With the exception of the last point, most of these requirements were achieved and incorporated into JCT 80.

Preparation of the 1980 edition of the Minor Works Form

By the mid-1970s however, it had become apparent that a more radical approach to the Standard Form of Building Contract was required and a draft 'short form' was approved by the RIBA Council in June 1978 and then submitted to the JCT for consideration. An appraisal of building contracts generally in 1980 by the RIBA established that 75 per cent of the work of 75 per cent of the architectural practices throughout the whole country was on contracts of less than £75,000 in value.

A JCT working party under the chairmanship of J. Barkey FRICS, a British Property Federation representative, was therefore set up in 1979 and after approval by all the constituent bodies a new edition of the Agreement for Minor Building Works was issued by the JCT in January 1980.

In the accompanying Practice Note (M1) the Tribunal pointed out the differences from the preceding edition, and in particular (notwithstanding the repetition of the title of the previous edition) the completely new, more logical sequence of clauses and the twelve new provisions.

Instead of the sentence at the end of the headnote:

'The Form is not appropriate for works for which bills of quantities have been prepared, or for which a schedule of rates is required for valuing variations'

the following, much longer sentence appeared instead:

'The Form is not for use for works for which bills of quantities have been prepared, or where the Employer wishes to nominate sub-contractors or suppliers, or where the duration is such that full labour and materials fluctuations provisions are required; nor for works of a complex nature or which involve complex services or require more than a short period of time for their execution.'

In spite of that, it was thought that architects would have no problem in using the form for appropriate work, and a practice note, published in the *RIBA Journal*, pointed out that this headnote had no legal validity. It was found, however, that in practice architects were reluctant to use MW 80 except in the circumstances prescribed, and the Joint Contracts Tribunal agreed to delete the headnote. A Practice Note, dated August 1981, was issued in place of the headnote and reads:

'(1)   The Form of Agreement and Conditions is designed for use where minor building works are to be carried out for an agreed lump sum and where an Architect or Supervising Officer has been appointed on behalf of the Employer.

(2)   The form is for use for Works for which a lump sum offer has been obtained based on drawings and/or specifications and/or schedules but without detailed measurements. It follows that those documents should be sufficient to enable the Contractor accurately to identify the Works to be done without the provision of bills of quantities by the Employer. Where the Works are of a complex nature a bill of quantities would ordinarily be necessary.

(3)   The form is for use where the period required for the execution of the Works is such that full labour and materials fluctuations provisions are not required.

(4)   Subject to the above, the form is generally suitable for contracts up to the value of £50,000 at 1981 prices.

(5)   In some contracts for which the form is used the Employer may wish to seek to control the selection of sub-contractors for specialist work. While this may be done by naming a person or company in the tender documents or in instructions on the expenditure of a provisional sum, there are no provisions in the form which deal with the consequences of what is, in effect, the nomination of a sub-contractor; nor is there any standard form of sub-contract which would be applicable to such selected sub-contractors. Such control of selection could also be achieved by the Employer entering into a direct contract with the specialist.

(6)   For Works where the criteria mentioned above do not apply reference should be made to the relevant JCT Practice Note [to be issued subsequently] for guidance as to the appropriate form to be used.'

The Practice Note forms no part of the contract and is misleading in the limitation it places on the form as generally suitable for contracts up to the value of £50,000 at 1981 prices.

The 1980 revisions

The new version retained the four-page format, relegating the provisions for tax fluctuations, VAT and statutory tax deductions by reference to a supplementary memorandum. The new form regrouped the existing clauses under the following headings:

(1) Intentions of the parties
(2) Commencement and completion
(3) Control of the works
(4) Payment
(5) Statutory obligations
(6) Injury, damage and insurance
(7) Determination
(8) Supplementary provisions

and in 1988

(9) Arbitration

In addition the following fourteen new provisions were also incorporated:

Recitals: A greater choice of what are to be regarded as contract documents.
Provision for naming a quantity surveyor.

Articles: Value added tax specifically excluded from the contract sum.
Arbitrators to be appointed by the President of the RIBA or RICS instead of the (then) Institute of Arbitrators.
Space for the contract to be entered into under seal.
A list of contents with decimal numbering.

Conditions
(1) The obligation of the contractor to comply with the contract documents (as in JCT 80).
(2) The duties of the architect enumerated (clause 1.2).
(3) The restrictions on assignment by the employer and contractor incorporated (clause 3.1).
(4) Provision for the contractor's representative (clause 3.3) and exclusion of persons from the works (clause 3.4).
(5) The employer is entitled to have other persons to carry out the architect's instructions if the contractor fails to comply within seven days (clause 3.5).

(6) Variations to be valued in accordance with the prices in the contract documents (clause 3.6).
(7) Reference to prime cost sums and cash discount deleted.
(8) Contradictions between the contract documents are to be corrected and treated as a variation if necessary (clause 4.1).
(9) Tax changes to be recoverable from the employer unless clause 4.5 is deleted.
(10) Increased costs not recoverable by the contractor (clause 4.6).
(11) The contractor to comply with statutory obligations (clause 5.1).
(12) Provision for the joint insurance of new works by the contractor (clause 6.3A).
(13) Provision for no further payments in the event of determination by the employer (clause 7.0).
(14) Provision for no further payments if the employer becomes bankrupt (clause 7.2).

A new standard form of building contract had therefore been created which, as the RIBA said in a contemporary practice note (*RIBA Journal*, March 1980), was now suitable for 'a wide range of contracts and could be appropriate for almost all contracts where bills of quantity are not prepared by the employer's professional advisers'. Since provision can be made for the naming of a quantity surveyor and provision for 'schedules' in certain circumstances, the form might be considered to be appropriate for use 'with quantities' also (for those additional 'schedules' being considered by some no more than a polite euphemism for bills of quantities). For the provisions necessary in those circumstances where its use with quantities is not appropriate, see Chapter 13.

Between April 1985 and July 1991 a number of Amendments were made to the form and are incorporated into the chapters that follow.

Chapter 1

The recitals and articles of agreement

The agreement, recitals and articles of MW 80 are little different from any other legal document beginning with the time honoured phrases: 'This Agreement is made the ... day of ... between ... Whereas ... Now it is hereby agreed as follows. As witness the hands of the parties hereto.'

Recitals: the work

Recitals normally do not form any part of the contract or create contractual obligations, but specify the assumptions and representations upon which the parties have undertaken the obligations contained in the contract.

In this case, however, the recitals are the only place in the contract where the exact nature of the work to be undertaken by the contractor is specified.

Care should be exercised in drafting this recital so that no opportunity can be afforded to the contractor to complain that variations subsequently ordered are of such a nature as to alter fundamentally the work he is being asked to undertake, to bring to an end his contractual obligations and to entitle him to be paid a *quantum meruit* for work done. This will rarely be the case but there have been occasions when the contractor has succeeded with this contention: *Holland, Hannen & Cubitt (Northern) Ltd* v. *WHTSO* (1981). For the avoidance of doubt, Amendment MW 7, which dealt with a number of miscellaneous revisions, was added in July 1991 to clarify this point.

Moreover, by clause 4.1, any inconsistencies between the various contract documents are to be treated as variations and priced accordingly.

First recital

The first recital defines the work the employer intends to be carried out. Apart from the point made above, this should present no problems provided that it is left in the most general terms and starts with a verb, e.g. 'to carry out alterations to *X*'s school in such and such a road' or 'to extend *Y* Ltd's factory in such and such street'. Only if the scope of the work is more specifically defined, e.g. 'to construct two new classrooms' or '... square metres of offices' are difficulties likely to arise, for a contractor may then justifiably establish that the scope of the contract has been substantially changed by a variation and the terms of the contract therefore no longer apply.

Naming the architect

The name of the architect under whose 'directions' the work is to be carried out is stated and his duties are subsequently enumerated in the conditions. It must be remembered that he is not a 'party' to the contract. He has two functions. The first is to act in an independent capacity as one who holds the balance fairly between the employer and the contractor. The other is to act as the employer's agent when he is specifically authorised to do so.

Whether the architect owes a duty to the contractor in tort not to negligently undercertify the value of work done or withhold other certificates, such as those for extensions of time, has been thrown into doubt by the decision of an Official Referee in *Pacific Associates* v. *Baxter* and in the Court of Appeal (1988). But that may well have turned on the special terms of the contract in that case and the long established rule that an architect owes a duty in tort to the contractor still exists.

The architect may be liable to his employer for breach of contract. He is no longer regarded as a quasi-arbitrator when certifying and is no longer protected from actions for negligence. In the case of *Sutcliffe* v. *Thackrah* (1974) an architect was held to be clearly under a duty to both parties to act 'fairly, reasonably and not vexatiously'. In this case the architects were acting both as architects and as quantity surveyors and were sued by the employer for certifying work which they knew had not been carried out correctly and the value of which they had not deducted from an interim certificate, so that the contractor who had become insolvent (as they always seem to do in these cases!) had been overpaid. The House of Lords overruled the earlier case of *Chambers* v. *Goldthorpe*, dating back to 1901, which until then had established the precedent, and held that the architect could not be considered to have been acting as a quasi-arbitrator since no 'dispute' had arisen, and the architect could therefore be sued by the employer for the negligent performance of his duties. The architect was now considered to have an obligation to act fairly but without immunity from legal proceedings should he be thought to have carried out his duties in a negligent manner – 'fairness without immunity' as the *RIBA Journal* succinctly put it in an article on the case the following December. He is however clearly under a duty to both parties to act 'reasonably' and not 'vexatiously'.

A footnote (a) to the first recital draws attention to the need to substitute the name 'Contract Administrator' for the 'Architect' when the name inserted is not that of an Architect, to comply with the requirement of the Architects (Registration) Acts 1931–64 whereby only those so registered could describe themselves as such. This amendment then enabled the form to be used by a local authority in which the head of the department is not an architect.

It is also important to remember to insert the name of the architectural practice or department of a local authority and not the name of an individual in case they subsequently leave their employment or are, for any other reason, no longer involved in the project.

Contract documents – selection, content and completeness

The question of precedence in the event of discrepancies between the contract documents is discussed in detail in Chapter 5. Nevertheless, it should be said here that, whereas MW 68 specifically excluded the use of bills of quantities or schedules of rates for valuing variations, this is no longer the case with MW 80. This now provides for different types of documents to be appended to the contract. Not only are 'schedules' now added to the 'drawings and specification' included as possible contract documents in the First Recital, but 'schedules of rates' are included in the Second Recital.

Drawings

Although the space for identifying the contract drawings (i.e. those actually provided to the contractor for the preparation of his tender) must be completed, there is currently no standard convention for their content. The contract drawings are, of course, intended to indicate to the tenderers and contractor on site the location and assembly of the materials and components, which are described elsewhere in the specification. The content of contract drawings was an early priority of the multi-disciplinary Committee for the Co-ordination of Project Information (CCPI), which was set up with representatives of architects, engineers, quantity surveyors and builders, but even after their recommendations were published, it is still necessary to rely on the competence of those preparing the drawings to ensure that all that is necessary for the accurate preparation of tenders is included.

Specification

This should not only cover workmanship and materials to be used but must also include all the other information necessary for the provision of comprehensive and accurate tenders, such further details as are necessary, e.g. access to the works, restriction of working hours, etc. It must be mentioned that the practice adopted in the United States, and by better architectural practices in the UK, of omitting all specification details from the drawings, or at least confining them to a separate panel, on all projects except those where there is only a single contract drawing has much to commend it if discrepancies arising from subsequent amendments are not to occur.

Schedules and schedules of rates

With the addition of the words 'schedules and schedules of rates' to the list of contract documents, MW 80 is now suitable not only for use with the traditional 'drawings and specification' type of contract but also for those in the repair and maintenance category, such as those required by hospital boards and local authorities where no drawings are required and the contract is let on the basis of a specification and a schedule of rates alone – even to the extent where it may be no longer 'lump sum' contract but more in the nature of 'cost plus' where the work executed is subject to subsequent remeasurement and the contractor reimbursed accordingly.

Quantities

Clearly there is a difference between the words 'schedules' and 'bills'. Whereas 'schedules of rates' do not by definition include any quantitative element, 'schedules' clearly do, since they are included separately, intended to be something different and there is no reason why some quantitative element should not be included in the schedules if this will ensure not only submission of more comparable and competitive tenders but also provide a more accurate basis for the valuation of variations by the architect. If the schedules are prepared entirely in accordance with the principles and rules of the current Standard Method of Measurement then this should of course be stated in the contract documents and attention similarly drawn to any departures from them.

It has been suggested that amendments would be necessary to use priced bills of quantities with MW 80 and they would have to be of such a nature and extent that brevity and simplicity, the main attraction of the agreement, would disappear.

That is surely not so. MW 80 can be, and has been, used successfully with full bills of quantities. The words of clause 4.2 'progress payments' and 'the value of any materials and goods which have reasonably and properly been brought on site for the purpose of the work' are quite adequate to enable the architect to make use of priced bills of quantities, if he so desires, in certifying progress payments.

Similarly, in pricing variations, specific provision is made in clause 3.6 for their valuation 'on a full and reasonable basis, using where relevant, prices in the priced specification, schedules and schedule of rates'.

The words 'priced ... schedules' are apt to describe priced bills of quantities.

Second recital

Pricing

For the first time in the Minor Works Agreement, provision was included in the recital in the 1980 Edition for the contractor to be required to price the specification, schedules or schedule of rates, thereby enabling variations to be based on them where relevant.

This, of course, has been the practice of the industry for many years, with architects adding a pricing column to the specification in their 'without quantities' contracts to enable them to arrive at a 'fair and reasonable' valuation of variations and interim progress payments, both usually originating from the contractor and without the need for the cumbersome 'Contract Sum Analysis' now included by the JCT in their 1981 Design and Build Contract.

However, in spite of what has been stated elsewhere, if an employer chooses to go out to tender on the basis of drawings plus MW 80 contract conditions, while it may be included elsewhere in the contract documents, i.e. the specification or form of tender, there is nothing in this document which requires the contractor to submit a schedule of rates. The reference to these in the second recital is merely an acknowledgement that if he has done so, they may be included in the recitals. It would appear from the first recital that a schedule of rates is not intended to be a contract document, notwithstanding reference to it in clause 3.6.

The question must then arise as to what happens if the employer has gone out to tender solely on the basis of drawings and the contract conditions and the contractor himself produces either a priced bill of quantities or a schedule of rates. The employer may wish to reject these, particularly if he takes the view that they have been 'front-loaded' or, if fluctuation clauses are included, have been 'back-loaded'.

It is submitted that the employer is under no obligation to accept these from the contractor and incorporate a schedule as contract documents or acknowledge the schedule of rates. Indeed, it may be said that it is usually disadvantageous to the employer to accept volunteered documents of this nature. MW 80 works perfectly well without them.

Third recital

Signing the contract documents
The recitals assume the parties have signed and therefore identified the contract documents. The courts will endeavour to give effect to the parties' intentions particularly where the work has already been executed even if the documents were not signed as was the case in *Tomkinson* v. *St Michael PCC* (1991). The earlier case of *Modern Buildings* v. *Limmer and Trinidad* (1975) also established that standard conditions can be incorporated in contracts by reference, even if the parties have never got round to signing the contract itself. In that case, in spite of an inaccurate description in an order from a main contractor to a nominated sub-contractor that he was to comply with 'the appropriate 1965 edition of the RIBA Form of Nominated Sub-contract' (which did not exist), the nominated sub-contractor had to comply with the conditions of 'the appropriate 1963 NFBTE/FASS Green Form' (which did exist).

Nevertheless it is essential to sign all contract documents if disagreements and disputes are to be avoided. This is particularly important because of the variable elements of the conditions such as those regarding commencement, completion, retention and defects liability period.

Fourth recital

Naming the quantity surveyor
For the first time in MW 80 provision is made for a quantity surveyor and any successor appointed in connection with the contract to be named. Nowhere else in the contract is he mentioned, and this is not dissimilar to the provisions in the JCT 'without quantities' forms, where there is provision for the quantity surveyor to value variations and make interim payments. If these are to be carried out by the architect when no quantity surveyor is appointed the architect's name should be entered here. Certainly if an architect intends to allow (as some do) the valuation of variations and preparation of interim certifies to be prepared by someone, probably better qualified and more competent than he is for these tasks, then it is desirable that the quantity surveyor should be named in the contract as well as the architect, and the contractor informed. Needless to

say, the naming of a quantity surveyor in recital 4 does not make him a party to the contract.

Should the 'schedules' have a quantitative element, have been prepared in accordance with the Standard Method of Measurement, as discussed earlier, and included in the contract documents, then the naming of the quantity surveyor who has prepared them is clearly desirable. Nevertheless, it must be pointed out that, since the architect is named in the later conditions as being responsible for valuing variations and progress payments, the naming of a quantity surveyor to whom the architect may in practice delegate these duties will in no way release him from his own legal liability for their accurate performance. Even under JCT 63 the quantity surveyor is a 'mere measurer', not impowered in any way to determine an employer's liability to pay: *Capital & Counties* v. *John Laing* (1983). And it is the architect, not the quantity surveyor, who is responsible for the issue of all certificates: *West Faulkner Associates* v. *London Borough of Newham* (1992), where the architect was held liable to the employer for failure to issue a determination notice under clause 25(1) of JCT 80 in spite of advice from the employer's quantity surveyor and solicitor not to do so.

It should also be noted that neither here, nor subsequently in the article where the replacement of the architect is dealt with, is there any provision for the right of reasonable objection by the contractor. This is in contrast to that provided in the JCT standard forms, in both 'with' and 'without quantities' editions.

Fifth recital

Guarantee/warranty schemes

Amendment MW4 published in October 1987 incorporated, by an additional fifth recital, provision for the incorporation of the warranty or guarantee schemes now being offered by some of the contracting and subcontracting organisations. This allows the employer to state if he intends to take advantage of such a scheme or not. If he does, then a new Supplementary Provision E has been provided. A new section 1, which incorporates by reference the necessary modifications to the conditions so that the extended BEC Guarantee Scheme for Small Building Works (currently for contracts up to the value of £50,000) can then apply. Should other contracting and sub-contracting organisations wish similar schemes to be included then no doubt further appropriate sections will be added also.

With the winding up of the BEC scheme for Small Building Works, this additional recital will no doubt be omitted in due course.

The articles of agreement

Article 1

The obligations of the contractor to 'carry out and complete the works' are fully set out in detail in the conditions, but it was nevertheless considered advisable to repeat them clearly and unequivocally in Article 1, with the addition by Amendment MW 7 in July 1991 that the Contractor not only had to carry out and complete the works but also any changes (variations) made in accordance with the contract conditions.

Sum payable: Article 2

Article 2 states the amount of the sum of 'consideration' which the employer will pay the contractor in return.

It is important to realise that the sum stated as payable in Article 2 is subject to the Supplementary Memorandum Part A (if this is incorporated) which begins with the words: 'The sum referred to in Article 2 shall be deemed to have been calculated in the manner set out below.' In short, Article 2 is deceptively simple and careful consideration should be given by an employer to the full terms of Part A.

As much of the work carried out by the contractor under this form of contract will not be zero-rated for value added tax, it is necessary to make specific reference to the fact that the contract sum and any other monies paid in accordance with the contract conditions are exclusive of VAT. For VAT will be due to be paid to HM Customs and Excise by the contractor and is subsequently recoverable from the employer in accordance with the detailed provisions of the Supplementary Memorandum. Only alterations to listed buildings are now zero-rated, guidance for which is given in Chapter 6.

Replacement of the architect: Article 3

In addition to repeating the name of the architect, the articles provide also for the appointment by the employer of any successor within a time limit of fourteen days and the particularly important and essential provision that no successor can 'disregard or overrule any certificate or instruction given by the architect for the time being'.

The effect of this is that the contractor is protected from the consequences of a conflict between the decision of the first architect and that of his successor on the same point with reimbursement of any financial consequences. This, of course, is subject to the rights of either party to arbitration, which might well be necessary in the event of the employer claiming some alleged negligence on the part of the architect in the performance of his duties.

Arbitration: Article 4

The detailed provisions for arbitration have now been moved, by Amendment 5 in 1988, from the articles back into a new Section 9 where they were in the original MW 80, and where they properly belong. They now differ little from those in JCT 80 but provide for *any* dispute arising at *any* time before or after practical completion to be referred to arbitration even after the determination of the employment of the contractor. The only exceptions are those in connection with VAT or statutory tax deductions covered by Parts B and C of the Supplementary Memorandum, as set out in Section 9. It should be noted that, in the event of disagreement between the parties, the appointment of the arbitrator no longer rests with the President or Vice-President of the Chartered Institute of Arbitrators but with the President or Vice-President of the RIBA or RICS.

The provisions for arbitration are fully discussed in Chapter 9.

The signatures of the parties

As has been said earlier, the lack of signatures to the contract does not invalidate it but, while not essential, signatures are clearly advisable. The provision of the necessary signatures on contracts under this form should present no difficulties. Contract documents are usually sent in duplicate first to the contractor and then to the employer for signature, and witnessed at the time of signature, by a secretary or an employee of each party. The documents are then returned to the architect who usually retains one set on the employer's behalf and sends one back to the contractor. Even if the contract has not been signed, the courts will still consider them to be enforceable and incorporate by reference *Tomkinson* v. *St Michael PCC* (1991).

Under hand or seal

The space at the head of the contents page of MW 80 is not left by accident but is provided at the request of the local authority constituent bodies on the JCT Tribunal for contracts to be entered into under seal when necessary.

The historic background and reasons for entering into a contract under seal are very clearly set out by John Parris in *The Standard Form of Building Contract: JCT 80*, in which he points out that, although since 1960 corporate bodies are no longer required to have their contracts under seal, as a matter of tradition many local authorities still do, although their primary reason is to extend the period in which an action for breach of contract is statute-barred from six to twelve years.

This may still be of importance as a result of the House of Lords decision in *Pirelli* v. *Oscar Faber* (1982).

From 1976, when the Court of Appeal decided the case of *Sparham-Souter* v. *Town and Country Developments*, it was possible to sue in tort for negligence or breach of statutory duty for failure to comply with the building regulations within six years of the time when the plaintiff first learned that he had a cause of action. This might be many years after a building was constructed and in fact in *McGuirk* v. *Homes (Basildon) Ltd* (1982) twenty years had elapsed before a house builder was held liable in damages for negligence and breach of statutory duty in the construction of a house. The House of Lords had expressly approved this principle in *Anns* v. *London Borough of Merton* (1977), where a building inspector had passed strip foundations over a previously existing cellar filled with uncompacted material, with the result that a block of flats tilted; the local authority, whose inspector had passed the foundations, was held liable in tort for negligence to the owners and occupiers of the flats.

However, late in 1982 in the *Pirelli* case, the House of Lords decided that the cause of action in tort arises not when a plaintiff knows that he has a cause of action because damage has become apparent, but when the damage occurs, even if he does not know of it. In this case, a factory chimney had been designed and erected in 1969 and proved defective. The plaintiffs, somewhat surprisingly, conceded that damage had taken place to it, unknown to them, in 1970, which was more than six years before they discovered the defects in 1978. The House of Lords held that the plaintiffs' action was statute-barred because more than six years had elapsed since the damage was suffered.

The Latent Damage Act 1986 attempted to deal with this and since *Pirelli*, cases have been struck out because the damage suffered occurred more than six years before the writ was issued, even though the plaintiffs had no knowledge of it.

The Latent Damage Act 1986 has done little to clarify the position for construction professionals as to liability for latent defects. Despite the stated intention of covering all forms of latent damage, discussion during Parliamentary debates and committee stages was confined virtually exclusively to the building industry

Defendants now have the protection of an action in tort for negligence being statute-barred six years from the date of the damage, or three years from the date of its discovery. There is a long-stop of 15 years from the date of any negligent act or omission.

Chapter 2

Intentions of the parties

It is interesting to note that although numerically the full JCT 80 standard forms now have forty clauses and GC/Works/2 thirty-seven, they all fit into the nine categories set out in MW 80:

(1) intentions of the parties
(2) commencement and completion
(3) control of the works
(4) payment
(5) statutory obligations
(6) injury, damage and insurance
(7) determination
(8) Supplementary Memorandum (on taxes)
(9) Settlement of disputes – arbitration

each with sub-clauses, making a total of thirty-three.

The intentions of the parties (clause 1.0)

The obligations of the contractor (clause 1.1)
While the express obligations of the parties appear to be set out clearly in MW 80, it must not be overlooked that the courts will also consider certain other obligations as incorporated into the contract by implication. The three most important implied terms in building contracts are that the builder will not only 'exercise reasonable skill and care' but will:

(a) carry out the work in a good and workmanlike manner
(b) use materials of a good quality and reasonably fit for their purpose
(c) ensure that the completed work will be reasonably fit for the purposes required.

There is a long series of judgments of the courts on these points stretching back over a number of years. There are various types of terms which will be implied in construction contracts. Two are of particular relevance: terms implied by operation of law and terms implied to give business efficacy to the contract.

The second category is based on the case of *The Moorcock* in 1889. It was concerned with a ship which, while discharging her cargo, suffered damage from settling on a hard ridge alongside the jetty when the tide went out. This case established that while there was no express term in the contract between the ship owner and the owner of the jetty that the berth was a safe one, this could be 'implied' because this was essential to the business efficiency of the contract, and it must be assumed to have been obvious to the parties without the need for any express provision for it in the contract itself.

In that case, if there are express terms in the contract relative to the same subject matter, a term cannot be implied. But in the case of terms imported by law they can supplement the express terms of the contract. For example, the case of *Young and Martin* v. *McManus Childs Ltd* (1969), dealing with a roofing sub-contractor, established that, even if a particular make of tile was specified by a developer/contractor, the sub-contractor still had an implied liability to ensure that the tiles used were of merchantable quality.

However, in the same year, in the case of *Gloucester County Council* v. *Richardson*, a supplier of precast prestressed concrete columns which developed serious cracks after they had been erected was relieved of his warranty by an express provision in his quotation. The main contractor, however, was not – a decision which John Parris, in his *Standard Form of Building Contract* concludes is unlikely to be repeated today.

In the case of *IBA* v. *EMI Electronics and BICC* (1980), which concerned a television mast, designed and built by a nominated sub-contractor (BICC), which collapsed in a storm, Lord Frazer said: 'It is now recognised that in a building contract for work and materials a term is normally implied that the main contractor will accept responsibility to his employer for materials provided by nominated sub-contractors ... and ought to be applied in respect to the complete structure including its design.'

Finally, in the case of *Holland, Hannen & Cubitt (Northern) Ltd* v. *Welsh Health Technical Services Organisation* in 1981, concerning *inter alia* defective windows, Judge Newey in giving his judgment noted that in the defence pleadings 'there were implied terms of the contract that the building work should be carried out in a good and workmanlike manner with proper skill and care with materials reasonably fit for the purpose', to which Cubitts did not file a reply and did not therefore dispute the alleged terms.

The contractor's express obligations

MW 80 apparently intends (as does JCT 80) to override these implied obligations by stating specifically that the contractor need only:

'... with due diligence and in a good and workmanlike manner carry out and complete the Works in accordance with the Contract Documents using materials and workmanship of the quality and standards therein specified ... '

This was presumably considered sufficient to satisfy the RIBA's insistence to the JCT in 1972 that the contractor should accept full responsibility for ensuring that the works complied with the contract documents. The contractor's obligation to comply with the building regulations, and any consequential conflict with the contract documents, are dealt with later in clauses 4.1 and 5.1.

To a non-lawyer this would seem to be perfectly clear and explicit, particularly the use of the words 'with due diligence'. Presumably this carries the dictionary meaning of 'steady application; industry', requiring the work to be proceeded with on a regular basis.

This has been defined by the courts in this country (there is also an Australian decision) in two cases: *London Borough of Hounslow* v. *Twickenham Garden Development Ltd* (1971) and *West Faulkner Associates* v. *London Borough of Newham* (1992) in which the judge said 'it was an unhappy one in its context'. He said:

'In the light of the judgments, text books and expert evidence, I consider that "regularly and diligently" should be construed together and that in essence they mean simply that the contractors must go about the work so as to achieve their contractual objectives.'

When the term 'with due diligence' occurs again in clause 7.1.1 as one of the two grounds for determination by the employer, it was presumably thought necessary to provide the additional reinforcement of 'or wholly suspends the carrying out of the Works before completion'.

Clause 1.1 however also includes the additional words:

'provided that where and to the extent that approval of the quality of materials or the standards of workmanship is a matter for the opinion of the Architect such quality and standards shall be to the reasonable satisfaction of the Architect.'

This unusually subjective standard rarely seen in other forms of contract did not occur in the 1968 version of the Minor Works Agreement and, apart from the restriction on the architect to be 'reasonable', it is clearly included to deny the contractor the opportunity to relieve himself of his contractual obligations for defects as happened in the case of *East Ham* v. *Bernard Sunley* (1966) where clause 30(7) of JCT 63, as it then stood, included the phrase 'which reasonable inspection or examination at any reasonable time during the carrying out of the Works ... would not have disclosed'.

That case dealt primarily with the finality of the final certificate and the right of the employer to subsequent arbitration. However it also established that the employer was entitled to the actual cost of making good damage when it was discovered, and not just the cost at the time of construction. It was said that defects could have been detected by 'reasonable inspection or examination at any reasonable time during the carrying out of the works or before the issue of the said [final] certificate' but not at the end of the defects liability period. Lord Upjohn added: 'I am at a loss to understand why a negligent builder should be able to limit his liability by reason of the fact that at some earlier stage the architect failed to notice some defective work.' The offending phrase was not however removed from JCT 63 until the July 1977 revisions.

While clearly such things as the pointing and colour of mortar in brickwork cannot be adequately specified in sufficient detail, architects must be sparing in including such terms in their specification, since a requirement for 'all work to be to the reasonable satisfaction of the architect', such as one used to see in specifications and bills of quantities, would effectively transfer all the responsibility for compliance with the contract documents from the contractor to the architect. This would perhaps be a matter of little consequence to employers, but one which few architects would wish to see. This is quite independent of the separate right of the employer to engage the architect to check that the contractor is complying with the contract documents and suing the architect if he negligently fails to do so. It does not relieve the contractor of his own responsibility to comply with his contractual obligations.

The architect's duties (clause 1.2)
The architect's duties under the terms of the contract are then stated in MW 80 as:

(1) to issue further information
(2) to issue all certificates (both those involving completion and those involving payment)
(3) to confirm all instructions in writing.

The manner in which the architect is to carry out these duties is detailed in later conditions, but not of course in the same degree of detail as in JCT 80. It must be emphasised again that the architect is not a party to the contract which is solely between the employer and the contractor, and that any other duties for which the employer may engage him, such as those set out in the 'Standard Form of Agreement', the RIBA's conditions of engagement, e.g. informing the client if the contract period or contract sum are likely to be materially exceeded, are entirely separate from those which the architect exercises as agent of the employer under the contract.

The question of 'further information' has always been unclear but it is accepted as a matter of practice that some further clarification of drawings and specification is generally required, and this additional information is issued in the form of architect's instructions, only those involving a variation to the contract, which may or may not have financial consequences, having to be so identified.

It must be remembered that the issuing of certificates includes both those involving completion and those involving payment. While only 'extensions of the time for completion' are required to be in writing under MW 80, it also requires the architect to '*certify* the date when ... the works have reached practical completion' and to '*certify* the date when, in his opinion, the contractor's obligations' for making good defects have been discharged. These are in addition to those certificates relating to progress payments, retention and the final valuation.

The confirmation of instructions in writing is included in the list of architect's duties and is covered in greater detail in the conditions in clause 3.5, which specifies the procedure for confirmation of oral instructions and the architect's powers in the event of the contractor's non-compliance.

Chapter 3

Commencement and completion

The employer's main concern, in addition to keeping the contract within the authorised expenditure limits, is probably to ensure that commencement and completion dates are maintained.

Instead of requiring the completion date to be included in an appendix, as in JCT 80, in MW 80 it appears within the conditions, with space for the date to be inserted in accordance with the tender particulars.

The date for commencement is given as that on which the Works 'may' be commenced. There is no obligation therefore on the contractor to take possession of the site on the date on which the employer can hand it over to him, and in theory at least, should he consider that the can assemble the whole of the contract works on site during the last week of the contract period he is perfectly entitled to do so. Should this happen of course he would need to have persuaded the architect that he was proceeding with 'due diligence' and would subsequently be able to carry out the works 'in a good and workmanlike manner' if the architect were not to determine the employment of the contractor in accordance with clause 7.1.

On the other hand, should the employer not be in a position to allow the contractor to commence work on the date stated, the courts have always held that this is a breach of contract, and the contract cannot be implemented until such time as the commencement and completion dates have been corrected, the new dates inserted, and any consequential financial adjustments incorporated in the contract sum entered in Article 2.

Failure to give possession of the site on the contractual date is an obvious breach of contract by the employer. However, unlike the JCT 80 contract, clause 22 of MW 80 may give the architect licence to extend the time for completion to cover this, so that it does not prevent the recovery of liquidated damages by making time at large, still less entitle the contractor to recover remuneration on a *quantum meruit* basis.

In contrast to the ICE conditions, under MW 80 neither the employer, nor the architect has any right to dictate to the contractor the sequence in which he is to carry out and complete the works. Any special requirements dictated by a particular project must be set out in the tender particulars and must subsequently be included in the contract documents. Even then the architect has no power under MW 80 either to vary the sequence in which the contractor proposes to execute the works or to postpone completion or any part. Were this to happen the contractor would, in turn, quite properly be entitled to determine the contract on the grounds that the employer had suspended the work under clause 7.2.3.

This is not to say, however, that the architect does not have some powers in this respect, since he can always (at his own peril) by an instruction vary the way in which the works are to be carried out by a variation under clause 3.6 without invalidating the contract. But the contractor will, of course, be entitled to reimbursement for the financial consequence of such a variation and will be paid accordingly.

The date for the completion of the works is, on the other hand, quite specific with the use of the word 'shall'. It does however give the contractor the option of completing the works before the contract completion date stated (the contract wording is 'by', not 'on'), and should this happen, the architect has no option but to issue his certificate under clause 2.4.

Should the employer not wish to accept the work prior to the contract completion date (for example, because of the risk of vandalism to the works before occupation), then this should be clearly stated in the tender documents so that the contractor can include for it in his tender price accordingly.

Extensions of the contract period (clause 2.2)

(Not as is sometimes incorrectly stated – extension of the date for completion since only a period and not a date can be extended.)

Compared to the complexities and detailed timetables of JCT 80, where clause 25 now runs to two and a half pages and includes thirteen relevant events which permit the architect to extend the contract period, MW 80 is refreshingly simple. Clause 2.2 states:

'If it becomes apparent that the Works will not be completed ... for reasons beyond the control of the contractor ... the contractor shall so notify the Architect who shall make in writing such extension of the time for completion as may be reasonable'

MW Amendment 5 in July 1988 added the clarification that 'reasons beyond the control of the contractor' did not include instructions issued because of a default of the contractor and included defaults of those employed or engaged by him and the suppliers of goods and materials but this does not apply to delays which are the fault of the employer. While there is no obligation on the contractor in the contract to supply a master programme, most architects will call for one in their tender documents, to enable them to discharge their separate duty to the employer 'to advise him if the completion of the works is likely to be delayed'.

It must again be emphasised that, although the provision of such a programme may be a contract requirement, its content is entirely a matter for the contractor and the architect has no power to do other than 'note it' and certainly never under any circumstances to 'approve' it. He does of course have power, as discussed earlier, to 'vary' it but if the contractor has any sense this will inevitably have financial consequences.

The obligation to apply for an extension to the contract period rests clearly with the contractor – clause 2.2. reads: 'if it becomes apparent ... the contractor shall notify the Architect'. The architect presumably has no power to extend the contract period unless he is so notified (not that this, in the author's experience, has ever arisen) and if it never does become apparent to the contractor that a delay has arisen then obviously no notification is made.

It is vitally important to note that the clause does not refer to delay in the progress of the works, but merely to the date for completion not being met. Delay in the progress of any part of the work does not of itself necessarily mean that an extension of time must be granted if reprogramming of a sector of the works, or the concentration of more labour over a shorter period, would enable the original completion date to be met.

It must also be noted that clause 3.6 now deals separately with mention of increased costs arising from delays to progress by the employer being recoverable by the contractor, either by direct loss and expense or in any other way.

'For reasons beyond the control of the contractor'
Under JCT 80 as amended, the architect can only grant an extension to the contract period if delay has been caused by one of the so-called 'relevant events', which stipulate specific reasons for delay beyond the control of the contractor. In MW 80, however *all* reasons beyond the control of the contractor are justifiable grounds for an extension to the contract period. This is not to say that the contractor is to be granted an extension on every occasion that delivery of materials to site is delayed or that one of his sub-contractors is off sick. As correctly argued by John

Parris (*The Standard Form of Building Contract*) delays in the quantity and quality of bricks to site are a matter for the contractor to sort out with the supplier involved and are not the concern of the architect, notwithstanding the fact that he specified them in the first place. It is no excuse that the materials and workmanship specified in the contract documents may be difficult to obtain or not readily available, since the contractor has contracted to provide them, without the proviso 'so far as procurable' that exists in JCT 80.

'Such extension of the time for completion as may be reasonable'

The obligation on the architect to exercise his judgment in extending the time for completion by a reasonable amount, without the imposition of a timetable, is again an example of the goodwill which should exist within the building industry; and the assumption that on the majority of contracts the parties will behave in a fair and reasonable manner, on the basis of mutual respect of each others' responsibilities, is a fact often overlooked in the dusty recesses of the offices of those solicitors and barristers who specialise in disputes on building contracts.

Not only in the valuation of variations but also in extensions of time for completion most builders know that if they have performed conscientiously throughout the contract, liquidated and ascertained damages may not be imposed after the contract date for completion and they will be awarded an appropriate extension for reasons beyond their control.

Damages for non-completion (clause 2.3)

However, should the contractor not be granted an extension of the contract period then clause 2.3 provides that the contractor shall pay liquidated and ascertained damages, at the appropriate rate per week inserted in the space provided in the contract, for every week or part of a week that the works remain incomplete after the original or extended contract completion date. Alternatively, as is usually the case, the employer may deduct such damages (Amendment 5 July 1988) since it was previously possible for the particularly astute contractor to insert that he be paid the full amount certified before he could refund the damages to which the employer was entitled.

It must first be pointed out that this is not, and never has been, a 'penalty' clause but solely a proper assessment of the financial damage the employer will suffer as a consequence of the works remaining incomplete. This will save the employer from having to resort to litigation in the courts for the necessary financial compensation arising from the delay to which he is entitled. It will also relieve him of the obligation to produce evidence to establish the actual amount, which he has to do if the damages are left 'at large'.

The amount of these liquidated and ascertained damages should not only include an appropriate amount to enable the employer to recover any additional professional fees for the post-contract services for which he might be liable as a result of the extended contract period and any consequential loss he has suffered due to delayed completion, but also a substantial amount to offset the amount of interim payments which the employer has made to date without gaining the benefit of the use of the works.

Many local authorities and hospital boards have a formula used for evaluation of the amount of the liquidated and ascertained damages. However, such a formula is not necessary and an employer does not have to justify the liquidated damages that a contractor has agreed.

Completion date (clause 2.4)

'Practical completion' was defined in *Westminster Corporation* v. *J. Jarvis & Sons* (1970) (by Lord Salmon) as meaning 'completion for all practical purposes, that is to say for the purpose of allowing the employer to take possession of the works and use them as intended'.

In *H.W. Nevill (Sunblest) Ltd* v. *William Press & Sons Ltd* (1981), Judge John Newey said:

> ' "Practical completion" means the completion of all the construction work that has to be done. . . . It follows that a practical completion certificate can be issued when owing to *latent* defects the works do not fulfil the contract requirements . . .
>
> The word "practically" . . . gives the architect a discretion to certify that [the contractor] has fulfilled its obligation . . . where very minor *de minimis* work has not been carried out.
>
> But if there were any *patent* defects in what [the contractor] had done the architect could not have given a certificate of practical completion.'

In *Emson Eastern Ltd* v. *E.M.E. Developments* (1991), the same judge held that where a contractor went into receivership after practical completion, any claim by the employer for damages suffered by the employer in having completion, remedial or snagging work carried out by another contractor had to be at common law and not under the contract. In other words, the certificate of practical completion was conclusive evidence that the 'Works' in clause 27.4.1 and 27.4.4 of the JCT contract Private

Edition without Quantities were completed. This principle clearly applies to all JCT contracts.

When the matter was discussed by the Joint Contracts Tribunal it was agreed that it was rarely in the best interests of the employer for him to have to wait for his building until every last screw was in place and every spot of paint scraped from the floor, as is technically required by the 'completion' demanded in the government GC/Wks/1 and 2 contracts.

In MW 80 all that is required of the architect is clearly set out in a simple sentence:

'The Architect shall certify the date when in his opinion the works have achieved Practical Completion.'

In practice, of course, he accompanies this certificate (as he does at the end of the defects liability period) with a list of those items still outstanding and will agree with the contractor a date on which he will carry out a further inspection to satisfy himself that the remaining items have been carried out and the works satisfactorily completed in all respects.

The simplicity of the clause must not however obscure the basic essential need for strict compliance with its requirement. For the issue of the certificate of practical completion sets the time for the start of the contractor's defects liability period. It also notifies the employer that the works are ready for his occupation and, more importantly, that he must now accept responsibility, not only for their subsequent maintenance, but also for their insurance against all future risks of damage by fire, flood and injury to third parties.

As Viscount Dilhorne said in 1970 in the case of the *City of Westminster* v. *Jarvis*, which concerned the discovery of a number of defective piles a month after the piling sub-contractor has left the site:

'It follows that a practical completion certificate can be issued when, owing to latent defects, the works do not fulfil the contract requirements and that under the contract the works can be completed despite the presence of such defects. Completion under the contract is not postponed until defects which become apparent only after the work has been finished have been remedied.'

Similarly, in *H. W. Nevill (Sunblest) Ltd* v. *William Press & Sons* (1981), a case where, because of defective drainage executed by a site works contractor in 1973 and not discovered until after practical completion the subsequent main contractor was delayed by four weeks until the drains had been repaired, Judge Newey held that, in addition to the remedies in JCT 63 clause 15, the plaintiff could also recover both damages and consequential loss notwithstanding that a certificate had been issued.

Finally it should be noted that the clause refers to 'practical completion' and not the more colloquial phrase 'the works being practically complete', with the implication that the works are almost but not quite complete.

Contrary to JCT 80 there are no provisions in MW 80 for partial occupation of the works with or without the contractor's consent.

Defects liability (clause 2.5)

The employer's interests against patent defects, 'excessive' shrinkage or any other faults which may appear during the defects liability period are adequately covered in MW 80 in clause 2.5. This period is often inaccurately described in this form, as in JCT 63 and JCT 80, as the 'maintenance period' although in fact this has nothing to do with 'maintenance' which is solely the responsibility of the employer. 'Maintenance' can be properly defined as the work necessary to stop a building falling into disrepair, whereas repair is that which is necessary to restore it to its proper condition. It has nothing to do with making good any defects in workmanship and materials during a defined period which is clearly stated as being the responsibility of the contractor.

This period was originally three months in MW 68, with the option of amendment, but in MW 80 a space has been left for the insertion of another period, no doubt in view of its suggested wider application for larger contracts and to allow the insertion of six months, which is usual for the majority of contracts, and/or the twelve months deemed prudent in respect of the heating and ventilating aspects of the work where, irrespective of the date of practical completion, it is considered necessary to monitor the performance of the heating system during the winter months, particularly when the installation of this part of the works is based on a performance specification.

The exclusion of the liability of the contractor for damage arising from frost after practical completion would appear an anachronism in this day and age of central heating, but no doubt the possibility of frost damage after practical completion could arise during winter months if the building were unoccupied, the central heating were not being used and it had not been drained down by the employer.

The phrase that defects should be made good by the contractor entirely at his own cost 'unless the Architect shall otherwise instruct' is as incomprehensible in MW 80 as it is in JCT 63 and JCT 80.

As John Parris quite rightly points out in *The Standard Form of Building Contract: JCT 80* 'the meaning attached to these words is obscure' to say the least, and in the event of such 'unbelievably generous employers' not being found, the architect would almost certainly be guilty of negligence. Certainly in the present author's experience no circumstances have ever arisen whereby defects in the contractor's workmanship or materials should have been put right at the employer's expense.

The final sentence in this sub-clause that:

'The Architect shall certify the date when in his opinion the contractor's obligations under this clause (2.5) have been discharged'

is as important as that in the preceding clause 2.4 with regard to practical completion. Here, however, the certificate does not initiate the employer's responsibility for any subsequent damage to the works but instead releases the contractor from any liability for subsequent patent defects in workmanship or materials. Of course in neither case in MW 80 is there any obligation placed on the architect to provide any justification of his decision. In both cases the matter is solely for his judgment ('in his opinion', using the time-honoured phrase of JCT 63 and 80) and nowhere in MW 80 is he required to give any explanation for his decision, any more than he is required to give any justification.

Lists of defective and outstanding items at practical completion and defects at the expiry of the defects liability period must always be prepared before the employer starts to use the building and also before the end of the defects liability period if subsequent arguments with the contractor denying responsibility are to be avoided.

Clause 2.5 was also amended in July 1991 (Amendment 7) to ensure that there was no doubt that defects in the works also included those executed as a variation in accordance with clause 3.6.

The case of *William Tomkinson & Sons Ltd* v. *The Parochial Church Council of St Michael in the Hamlet with St Andrew Toxteth in the City and Diocese of Liverpool and Holford Associates*, decided by Judge Stannard, sitting as Official Referee in Liverpool in August 1990, concerned the renewal of window frets and reroofing carried out in September 1984 under a JCT MW 80 contract. In addition to establishing the status of an unsigned contract, the architect's authority to accept a tender on the employer's behalf, and the definition of a 'storm' for insurance purposes, there were no less than six issues relating to clause 2.5 dealing with the contractor's liability for defects. The Judge held, when the contractors left uncovered an access hole they had formed in the roof and the organ was damaged beyond economic repair by rainwater entering the building during a storm the following night, that in each case:

(1)   The employer was only entitled to the cost of the remedial work executed by the contractor.

(2)   Notice of defects can be given orally under MW 80 and does not have to be in writing.

(3)   The words 'defects which appear within three months of the date of practical completion' in clause 2.5 extend to defects which appear before practical completion.

(4)   Defects arising from excessive shrinkage or other defaults are not qualified by any reference to 'the works' and therefore extend to existing structures also.

(5)   'Workmanship not in accordance with the contract' also covers existing plasterwork damaged by the contractor, failure to deal with dry rot, litter not cleared away and a ceiling damaged by a bracket dropped on it by the contractor.

(6)   The true measure of the damage was not the cost to the church of making good the damage but the cost to the contractors of making good the damage had they been so required.

Chapter 4

Control of the works

Whereas the clauses dealing with commencement and completion may be the most important to the employer, those dealing with the control of the works are of the greatest concern of the architect.

Assignment (clause 3.1)
A clause precluding either the employer or the contractor from assigning the contract without the written consent of the other did not appear in the earlier 1968 edition, but is now included in MW 80 as clause 3.1 which uses identical words to those in JCT 80 clause 19.1. Whereas situations will obviously arise when a contractor, forced by a change in his circumstances or work load, might wish to sub-contract the work to another firm or individual, it would seem far less likely in the case of an employer. However an employer may wish to dispose of a property before alterations are completed or he may find himself with insufficient funds part way through a contract and such instances have certainly occurred on contracts for speculative office blocks.

Clause 3.1 in MW 80 was considered by the Court of Appeal in *Linden Garden Trust Ltd* v. *Lenestra Sludge Disposals Ltd* (1992). The court held that its effect was the same as clause 17(1) of JCT 63 (and impliedly clause 19.1 of JCT 80).

It meant that the contractor could not delegate his obligations under the contract by sub-contracting all of them. But, contrary to the statement in *Keating on Building Contracts*, 5th edition p. 539, it did not prevent a contractor assigning to a third party payments due by the employer to him.

At common law, the obligations of a contract cannot be assigned: *Nokes* v. *Doncaster Amalgamated Collieries* (1940). Clause 3.1 of MW 80 prevents the assignment of both the burden and the benefits. However, the right to sue for breaches of contract can be assigned, it was held in the *Linden Garden Trust* case.

It was heard at the same time as *St Martin's Corporation and Martin's Investments Ltd* v. *Sir Robert McAlpine & Sons Ltd* (1992). The two plaintiffs were associated companies, both owned by Kuwaiti interests. The first had entered into a contract in the JCT 63 form with the defendants to build a shopping centre in Hammersmith. To avoid liability for British taxation the Corporation assigned the title to the property to the investment company. The deed of assignment included 'the full benefits of all contracts and agreements whatsoever entered into by the Assignor and existing at the date hereof for the construction and completion of the development'.

There was no attempt to procure the consent of Robert McAlpine & Sons, and the Court of Appeal held that the deed of assignment was void, since it violated the provisions of clause 17(1) of JCT 63.

Sub-contracting (clause 3.2)

It is regrettable that, today, a far smaller proportion of the work on a building contract is carried out by direct employees of the main contractor. Indeed the present author has experience of at least one project on which it would appear that the only employee of the main contractor on site was the general foreman.

MW 80 clause 3.2 therefore repeats clause 5 of the earlier edition in a similar way so as to prevent a contractor chosen for his particular capabilities assigning his responsibilities for the proper performance of the contract to another without the knowledge and consent of the architect.

It must be pointed out that the obligation on the contractor is to notify the architect merely of which part of the work he proposes to sub-contract, and not to whom. Technically, therefore, the architect has no right to demand the name or details of the firm or persons the contractor intends to use. However, while the architect's 'consent shall not be unreasonably withheld', it is common practice and commonsense for the architect to request, and for the contractor to provide, details of the firm or individuals to whom the contractor intends to entrust the particular section of the work. This consent, of course, in no way relieves the contractor of his own responsibility for its satisfactory execution, and the sub-contractor concerned remains a 'domestic' sub-contractor of the main contractor in the full sense of the word.

It is always prudent for the architect to enquire at the commencement of a contract which, if any, part of the work the contractor intends to sub-contract, and should the sub-contracting firms be unknown to him, he should send to three architects for whom the sub-contractor has previously worked a short questionnaire similar to that shown in Figure 2.

Should the answer to the last, but most important of all questions – 'would you use them again' – be in the negative, this is clearly all the evidence that is necessary to establish that the architect's consent is not unreasonably withheld.

Finally, it must be pointed out that there is no provision in the contract for 'artists and tradesmen' to be directly employed by the building owner concurrently on the works. Should this be necessary, it must either be included in the tender documents or, if later, during the execution of the works with the consent of the contractor.

The contractor's representative (clause 3.3)

Clause 4 of MW 68 required that the contractor 'shall at all reasonable times keep upon the works a competent person in charge'. In the related clause 3.3 of MW 80 the additional requirement has been added that any instructions given to him by the architect shall be deemed to have been issued to the contractor. The use of the phrase 'competent person in charge' instead of the time-honoured description 'foreman' mirrors JCT 80.

There is no truth in the suggestion that the JCT adopted the present wording to avoid the need to refer also to a forewoman or foreperson in charge, but it clearly reflects current practice with the present wide variety of job descriptions ranging from 'general foreman' through 'site agent' to 'contract manager'.

Irrespective of nomenclature, it is obviously essential that the contractor's representative or agent on site is clearly identified so as to avoid instructions being given to or by the wrong person. In the case of *Clayton* v. *Woodman & Son* (1962), for example, an architect disregarded the advice of an experienced bricklayer that it would be better to pull down an existing wall than cut a chase into it for a new concrete floor. The bricklayer was injured when the work was carried out without the necessary shoring and support specified. For an architect to tell the contractor to carry out the work without support would not only have altered the contract, but would have been outside his own competence and would have made him immediately liable for negligent advice. The way in which the works are executed are entirely a matter for the contractor.

The opposite situation arose two years later in the case of *Clay* v. *Crump* (1964). Here, in a telephone conversation, the architect on the advice of a demolition contractor, agreed to an existing wall to be left

FIRM:

WORKS CARRIED OUT:

Please enter details or tick box as appropriate:

YEARS

1. How long have you known this firm? ☐

2. What do you consider the maximum value of any one contract this firm is capable of executing?

AMOUNT

£

How would you assess the following:-

		POOR	REASONABLE	GOOD	EXCELLENT	COMMENTS
3.	Their office organisation and management capabilities.	☐	☐	☐	☐	
4.	Their ability to formulate practical programmes.	☐	☐	☐	☐	
5.	Their ability to maintain programme.	☐	☐	☐	☐	
6.	Their standard of workmanship.	☐	☐	☐	☐	
7.	Their site organisation.	☐	☐	☐	☐	
8.	Their conduct of labour relations.	☐	☐	☐	☐	
9.	Their relationship with sub-contractors and statutory authorities.	☐	☐	☐	☐	
10.	Their attention to site welfare and safety.	☐	☐	☐	☐	
11.	Their degree of co-operation.	☐	☐	☐	☐	

		YES	NO
12.	If the firm was the main contractor, did they rely extensively on sub-contractors?	☐	☐
13.	If the firm was the main contractor, were there any problems with payments to sub-contractors and suppliers?	☐	☐
14.	Were defects remedied promptly?	☐	☐
15.	Were final accounts settled satisfactorily?	☐	☐
16.	Would you use this firm again?	☐	☐

Figure 2

standing on site without support. Although he subsequently visited the site, he did not inspect the wall, neither did the main contractor, having assumed the architect had in fact done so. When the wall subsequently collapsed the demolition and main contractors as well as the architect were all held to be liable for the injury to one of the main contractor's men.

It should be noted that the identity of the 'person in charge' is not a matter for the approval of the architect, nor is his consent necessary should the contractor wish to replace him. The choice of a representative, with the necessary qualities and capabilities, is clearly the sole responsibility of the contractor and is a matter on which the architect should have no say. To have a succession of foremen, with different trade experience and capabilities, may well be an advantage on some contracts, but this is rarely the case, and for this reason most architects include in their tender documents the requirement that the foreman shall not be changed without adequate prior notice.

It should also be noted that the words of MW 68 'at all reasonable times' have been substituted in MW 80 for 'constantly', since, taken literally, this would imply round-the-clock attendance, instead of the normal working hours which is presumably what is meant by 'at all reasonable times'.

It is important to note that in MW 80 there is no express provision for access to the works either for the architect or for a clerk of works as the architect's representative, this being presumably an implied condition of the contract.

Exclusion from the works (clause 3.4)

Contrary to the position with regard to the contractor's representative, the architect has every right to object to the employment of certain individuals on the site, should he consider them incompetent or their behaviour offensive.

MW 80 has therefore introduced, in clause 3.4, a provision similar to that in JCT 63 and 80.

The phrase used in JCT 63 providing for 'dismissal from the Works of any person thereon', while correctly referring to dismissal from the *works* and not from the employment of the contractor, could clearly be misinterpreted, particularly in a period when the employment of employees is protected by such legislation as the Employment Protection Act 1975. The words 'exclusion from the works' used in MW 80 clause 3.4 are therefore identical to that in clause 8.5 of JCT 80.

Architect's instructions (clause 3.5)

It was mentioned earlier, with regard to the architect's duties under MW 80 clause 1.2, that all instructions are to be confirmed in writing and this is repeated in clause 3.5, with the additional requirement that the contractor must carry them out forthwith.

The definition 'forthwith' is obscure but according to *Osborn's Concise Law Dictionary* 'forthwith' is defined as 'as soon as reasonably can be'. Similar uncertainty is attached to the requirement for oral instructions to be confirmed in writing in two days.

JCT 80, and formerly JCT 63, go to elaborate lengths with regard to the confirmation of any oral instructions (note the correct use of the adjective 'oral' and not the inaccurate 'verbal' so often used loosely). These include a provision for the contractor to confirm them within seven days and the architect to dissent within a further seven. However MW 80 does not envisage any such instructions other than those in clause 1.2 which require the architect to 'confirm all instructions in writing', from which it may be inferred that the use of the word 'confirm' acknowledges that some instructions may in practice be given orally.

This is evidenced in the later requirement in clause 3.5 for oral instructions to be confirmed in writing by the architect within two days (but without any guidance as occurs in JCT 80 as to whether these are 'working days' or not).

Had it been intended that this meant two working days, the contract would surely have said so, and presumably the shorter period of two days, compared with the seven plus seven in JCT 80, arises from the shorter contract period which is likely when MW 80 is used, and from the need to have instructions implemented more quickly even if it means, for example, that an instruction given on site on Friday afternoon should strictly be confirmed in writing to the contractor by lunchtime the following Sunday to be legally binding.

It should be noted that there is no restriction on the way in which architect's instructions should be confirmed in writing. Although many architects adopt the discipline of using pre-printed forms, instructions by letter, handwritten in duplicate on pads on site, or typewritten in memoranda of weekly or fortnightly site meetings (provided they are issued within two days of the meeting) are all equally binding on the contractor under MW 80.

It should also be noted that there is no provision in MW 80, as there is in JCT 80 clause 4.1, for the contractor to object to an instruction requiring a variation. Nor is there any provision, as in JCT 80 clause 4.2, for the architect to specify in writing the (contract) condition under which he is issuing the instruction, or for the matter to be submitted to immediate arbitration in the event of the contractor refusing to comply.

MW 80 simply allows the architect to issue written instructions which the contractor shall carry out forthwith.

The option of the employer to engage others (clause 3.5)

Should these instructions not be carried out within seven days of written notice, MW 80 empowers the employer to employ and pay others to carry them out and to deduct the cost as a debt from monies due to the contractor. This provision did not occur in MW 68 and now gives the employer the same rights as he had in JCT 63 and now has in JCT 80 clause 4.1, using the identical words.

There is no specific reference in MW 80 to immediate arbitration and in the event of the contractor refusing to comply with an instruction, this is not considered in itself a 'dispute' any more than is failure to perform.

Variations – who evaluates them and how? (clause 3.6)

MW 80 clause 3.6 gives the architect the same powers as he had in MW 68 clause 2(ii) to order an addition to, omission from, or change in the works or a change in the sequence or period in which the works are to be carried out.

This clause is, of course, essential from the employer's point of view since without it no variations could be incorporated in the works without the risk of the contractor repudiating the contract on the grounds that it had been invalidated by the variation and he required a new contract before incorporating the variation. This can arise, of course, if the instruction were such that the contractor could persuade the court or arbitrator that the whole scope of the contract had been changed from that originally undertaken.

It is important to note also that it is the architect who is named as the one empowered to vary the work and not the employer, and the architect is thereby given the authority to act and issue instructions on the employer's behalf which he would otherwise not have and as has been confirmed in *Tomkinson* v. *St Michael PCC* (1991).

The implications of this, however, are that even if the architect did not have the employer's authority to issue such a variation (since the RIBA Standard Form of Agreement for the Appointment of an Architect (SFA/92) clause 1.2.4 requires him to 'make no material alteration to or addition to or omission from the services without the knowledge and consent of the client'), the contractor must carry them out, and will be paid for them, since, notwithstanding that they were carried out without his consent, the employer is legally estopped from denying that such variations were legally instructed.

MW 68 and MW 80 both continue with the provision for the valuation of these variations 'by the Architect on a fair and reasonable basis' – the valuation, as in the standard forms, being solely the responsibility of the architect without any requirement for the agreement or even the presence of the contractor.

In practice, as we all know, while architects have to keep the employer informed of their estimation of the value of variations to date during the progress of the works, on contracts of this nature variations are usually valued on the basis of a claim submitted by the contractor on completion of the works, and this claim is generally accepted by the architect provided that, in his opinion, it is 'fair and reasonable'. Should this not be the case, then the architect must decide what, in his opinion, the value should be. Should the contractor not agree and the sums involved are substantial enough, then the matter would have to be referred to an arbitrator appointed under Article 4 and clause 9.

MW 80 clause 3.6 contains the additional phrase 'using where relevant prices in the priced specification/schedules/schedule of rates', the document to be priced being that which was stated in the new recital 2. Here again the contract reflects what is considered good practice in the industry, in this case the practice of architects and surveyors providing a column in their specifications so that not only can the cost of the works included in the tender be apportioned and checked, but the cost of any variations can also be evaluated on the same basis. Should the prices in the specification for any reason not be similar to those in the priced specification or schedules (for example, because the quantity or the conditions under which the specification was drawn up have varied significantly), then the variations must be valued on a 'fair and reasonable' basis as provided for earlier.

MW 80, however, has no proviso such as that in the JCLI Form of Agreement for Landscape Works that if any omission substantially varies the scope of the work, such valuation shall take due account of the effect on any remaining items of work; nor does it give any indication as to the meaning of 'relevant' or the procedure to be adopted when they are not considered to be relevant. Without becoming involved in the complexities and detail of JCT 80, the same basic principles clearly apply and are as good a basis as any:

- Similar work under similar conditions to be valued in accordance with the prices in the contract documents.

- Similar work under dissimilar conditions to be valued in accordance with rates based on the prices in the contract documents.
- Work not of a similar nature to be valued on a fair and reasonable basis.
- Work which cannot be properly measured to be valued at daywork rates.

The MW 80 clause ends with a similar provision to that in JCT 80 allowing the employer to agree with the contractor for the valuation of a variation to be on a different basis. In the case of MW 80, however, the power is vested in the architect with the words:

'Instead of the valuation referred to above the price may be agreed between the Architect and the Contractor prior to the Contractor carrying out any such instruction.'

Direct loss and expense
There is now provision in MW 80 by Amendment 5 in July 1988 to clause 3.6 for the recovery by the contractor on a contractual basis of any payments due to him for the reimbursement of any direct loss and expense he has incurred arising from a variation, carried out under an architect's instructions, which affects the regular progress of the works.

Should the contractor incur any such direct loss and expense, or any consequential loss, there is now provision in MW 80 for him to receive additional payment, if the regular process of the work is affected, and the valuation of the variation is to include in it any direct loss and/or expense incurred by the contractor.

Provisional sums
Where sufficient information about work required to be included in a building contract is not available at the time of the preparation of tender documents, either because the employer's requirements cannot be adequately ascertained or because the true extent and scope of the work cannot be established until work has started on site, the cost is estimated by the architect, and included in the tender documents under the description 'provisional'. When, in due course, these details are known, the architect instructs the contractor to omit these sums and either to carry out the work himself or to place his order with an appropriately qualified specialist.

If at the outset it is known that the work will have to be carried out by specialist sub-contractors then the sum to be included is allowed for as a 'provisional' sum.

In MW 68 clause 2(iii) provided for the architect to issue such instructions as were necessary for the expenditure of prime cost sums and for such work to be valued on a fair and reasonable basis. No such distinction exists in MW 80.

The provisional sums and the selection of specialist sub-contractors

As has been discussed earlier, much of the work on building sites today is carried out by sub-contractors. Some work, such as the eradication of dry rot or damp proofing, may require specialist skills. In the case of other work, such as electrical wiring or floor tiling, the contractor may not have sufficient work of that nature to keep specialists on his own staff continually employed.

Where the architect wishes to retain the choice of these sub-contractors himself, he has traditionally adopted the practice either of naming them in the tender documents or of including a provisional sum. The disadvantage to the contractor of the latter is that at the time of tender he does not know either the identity of some of his intended sub-contractors (which in some projects may involve a substantial proportion of the work), details of any special requirements for attendance for which he should allow or the period such sub-contractors will require to carry out the work on site.

MW 68 clause 2 continued with the requirement that all sub-contracts which the contractor had to enter into as a consequence should include a cash discount of $2\frac{1}{2}\%$ in the case of sub-contractors, and 5% for suppliers, to be retained by the main contractor if payment was made within 14 days of the date the contractor was due to have received it from the employer, in the case of sub-contractors, and within 30 days of the end of the month during which the materials were delivered in the case of suppliers.

In practice, the necessity for these discounts was often overlooked by architects and they were incorporated by sub-contractors and suppliers adding one thirty-ninth or one nineteenth to their tenders. Many contractors tended to look on these discounts as part of their profit element and deduct them whether the payment was made promptly or not.

In their proposals for MW 80 the RIBA deleted the provisions for cash discount from this clause, as they had been advocating should also be done in the Standard Form.

The contracting and sub-contracting representatives on the Joint

Contracts Tribunal were prepared to agree to this provided the reference to prime cost sums was deleted as well, since they considered that the provisions for the nomination of sub-contractors, particularly with regard to direct payment and early final certificates, were far from adequate.

This was therefore done and only that part of the clause referring to provisional sums was kept in MW 80 as clause 3.7, with the headnote referred to earlier stating that the form was not suitable for use 'where the Employer wishes to nominate sub-contractors or suppliers'.

This the RIBA was prepared to accept, considering that the headnote had no legal validity and that architects could still name sub-contractors when they considered it necessary using the provisional sum clause. They issued a practice note in the *RIBA Journal* (August 1980, p. 91) in due course to this effect.

This practice note pointed out that MW 80 could be used when the architect wished to influence or control the selection of these specialist sub-contractors in one of four ways:

- *Firstly* by the careful check on any such sub-contractors as the main contractor intended to employ under clause 3.2. This in practice would only be of limited use being little more than the power of a veto.

- *Secondly* by restricting the main contractor to use only those named in a list in the tender documents in a similar way to that provided in JCT 80 clause 19, the difference being that in MW 80 there is no lower limit to the number of firms to be listed (in many instances such as dry rot eradication the architect might wish to restrict the main contractor to a single firm) – but in this instance the details of the work would have to be finalised sufficiently early for them to be included in the contract documents.

- *Thirdly* by having the work executed as a direct contract between the employer and sub-contractor, this being only suitable for items such as landscaping or floor finishes and not where the specialist work bears a complex programme relationship with that of the main contract.

- *Fourthly* by issuing instructions under clause 3.7 for the acceptance of a tender from a particular sub-contractor or supplier. There is no specific provision in the form for prime cost sums but that does not amount to a prohibition of their use. However the absence of detailed provisions relating to nominated sub-contractors and suppliers means that provisional sums should be used for nomination only where there is known to be very little likelihood of a dispute between the main contractor and the architect's nominee. Care should be taken that attendance, discounts and programme are established between parties in advance.

Architects were not however prepared to disregard such a strong 'health warning' in the headnote and in April 1982 MW 80 was printed without the headnote but with the accompanying practice note M2, referred to earlier in the Introduction, setting out the position in similar terms to those used by the RIBA.

The position therefore now is that, where the architect using MW 80 intends to restrict the contractor to the use of a single sub-contractor of his own choosing, a clause such as the following should be included in the contract specification:

'Include the provisional sum of £ .... for .... work to be executed by a specialist sub-contractor selected by the Architect. Add for profit and attendance.'

Additionally, if the identity of the sub-contractor concerned is known at the time of the invitation to tender, the name of the proposed specialist sub-contractor should be inserted, and whenever possible the period the sub-contractor requires to execute his work. This eliminates any subsequent claims by the main contractor that he had allowed a shorter period when tendering.

This clause has been used by the present author's own practice for the past ten years without any difficulty. It must be remembered, however, that it implies no design input by the specialist sub-contractor, hence no employer/sub-contractor agreement, and possible loss of liquidated and ascertained damages by the employer in the event of the main contractor being delayed by the sub-contractor concerned. Nor is there any provision for direct payment to the specialist sub-contractor in the event of default by the main contractor.

When there is an element of design by the specialist sub-contractor, as in heating, ventilating or electrical work, this can best be dealt with either by using a suitably adapted version of NSC2 or 2a or by ensuring that the sub-contractor concerned is a member of a trade organisation such as the Confederation of Registered Gas Installers (CORGI), the Heating and Ventilating Contractors Association (HVCA) or the Electrical Contractors Association (ECA), all of whom operate schemes for the rectification of defective work by their members at no cost to the employer.

Naming

It has been said that nomination is only justified for one of three reasons:

(1)   if early ordering was necessary
(2)   if a particular quantity was required
(3)   if a particular expertise or quality was involved.

Nomination can however be avoided and no problems will arise if either a single firm or list of firms with the work fully described is included in the tender documents prepared by the architect. In this case the contractor · can invite tenders from the firm or firms named at the same time as those he is sending out to the other sub-contractors to whom he intends to delegate those part of the work he does not propose to carry out himself, and for whom he assumes the necessary consents will, in due course, be forthcoming from the architect. The lowest tender from the named firms is then included in his offer.

It is true that this procedure may involve the architect in providing each main contractor with sufficient copies of the drawings and specification for each sub-contractor included in his list, but the suggestion that it does not produce the lowest tenders and destroys the confidentiality of the main contractor's tender list is quite unfounded, since the lowest price submitted from sub-contractors of known reliability will presumably be included by those contractors tendering, and all his special requirements for attendance and programme will be included with those of the main contractor also.

In the case of *Terry Pincott* v. *Fur and Textile Care Ltd and Others* (1985), concerning a Minor Works contract to the value of just over £105,000, £60,000 of which was to be carried out by specialist sub-contractors, Judge Smout held that an architect was negligent in wrongly advising a main contractor to enter into a sub-contract in the belief that he was not responsible for any work other than his own.

In this instance the architect (who was both eighth defendant and third party in a case with five counsels and four firms of solicitors, lasting 50 days) wrongly advised the main contractor that he would have no responsibility for the specialists' work on a contract for alterations and extensions to a dry cleaning shop in St John's Wood. The situation was further complicated by the fact that no planning consents, building regulation approvals or party wall awards were obtained, neither was any time allowed for the completion of the specialist sub-contract works. As a consequence the employer refused to make any payments until the work was completed, the architect resigned and much of the work had to be rebuilt.

Standard forms of sub-contract and tender

Whereas the ICE and JCT 80 forms of contract both have standard forms of sub-contract, the latter with one produced by the JCT for nominated sub-contractors, and another (DOM/1) by the Building Employers Confederation (BEC) for domestic sub-contractors, none has been produced by the JCT for the Minor Works Form.

The advantages of such a form are obvious: each party knows that it is compatible with the main form and is familiar and experienced in its use, all aspects and each party's interests are fully covered, with any special requirements clearly identified.

Whereas the JCT 80 sub-contract forms run to 40 or more pages, on account of the detailed provisions of the main form, this would not be necessary for MW 80 where the same form could be used for sub-contractors chosen by the architect and those chosen by the main contractor alike. A suitable form used by the present author is included as Appendix B.

Chapter 5

Payment

While the contract clauses of most interest to employer and architect may be those dealing with completion and with the control of the works respectively, those which concern the contractor most are almost certainly those dealing with payment and MW 80 clauses such as 4.1 dealing with payment on account of the errors of the architect in particular.

In their original proposals for the new short form the RIBA included this clause with the other duties of the architect in MW 80 clause 1.2, but when it was presented to the Council it was pointed out that it was hardly tactful to begin a contract with a clause dealing with the errors of the architect, and it was moved to the section dealing with payment, where no doubt contractors felt it was more relevant anyway.

Discrepancies within the contract documents (clause 4.1)
There has always been discussion between the lawyers as to the validity of JCT 63 clause 3(3) which provides that 'nothing in the Contract Bills shall override or modify the application or interpretation of that which is contained in the Articles of Agreement, the Conditions or the Appendix', this being contrary to the legal convention that the particular detailed provisions take precedence over the standard general ones, and also that, other than specifically stated departures from the Standard Method of Measurement, any other departure, error in description, quantity or omission should be paid for by the employer. Whether or not the employer can recover from the architect will depend on the courts, as shown in the following cases.

In *Williams* v. *Fitzmaurice* (1858) a house was to be completed, dry and fit for Major Fitzmaurice's occupation by 1 August 1858. The sum to be paid was £1100 and no flooring was mentioned in the specification. The contractor refused to put in flooring unless he was paid extra for it and the employer was held to be justified in turning the contractor off the site, and fixing the flooring already bought on to the site by the contractor to complete the works without paying the contractor the amount outstanding under the contract. Nor did he have to pay the cost of the flooring since, although this was omitted from the specification, 'it was clearly inferred from the language of the specification that the plaintiff was to do the flooring' – a view that is unlikely to prevail today.

The case of *Patman and Fotheringham* v. *Pilditch* (1904), was on a contract of £17,000 based on plans, invitation to tender specification and bills of quantities, which included everything necessary, whether described in the specification, shown on the drawings or not, without any express provision for the measurement of the works. It was held that if the quantities were less than those required by the drawings, the contractor was entitled to be paid an appropriate addition to the contract sum.

In a further case, *Wilkes* v. *Thingoe RDC* (1954), Judge Caswell, sitting as Official Referee, decided that where a contract provided for a smaller number of cookers than there were houses 'the architect was liable to his employers, who, had they known the true cost of completion, would have effected savings elsewhere'.

JCT 80, however, incorporates an additional clause 2.3 which provides that *if* the contractor finds any discrepancy in or divergence between any of the contract documents, he shall immediately give the architect written notice who will then instruct the contractor accordingly.

Inconsistencies

MW 80 clause 4.1 incorporates a similar clause but without the requirement of the contractor to notify the architect nor for the architect to issue instructions. All that it states is that any inconsistency shall be corrected and if the correction involves a change, it shall be treated as a variation.

This, in the present author's opinion, is a masterly piece of drafting by the Tribunal, leaving every case to be decided on its merits, the judgment of the architect and agreement between the parties, not even dealing with the financial consequences except to say that the change may involve a variation and therefore, by implication, a financial adjustment to the contract sum.

Precedence

MW 80 clause 4.1 continues in a similar way to JCT 63 and 80 to repeat that the contract conditions take precedence over the drawings and specification. It is a matter of regret, and no doubt something which could with advantage be incorporated in future editions of the form, that no guidance is given to the precedence of the remaining documents.

This should not be difficult and a clause such as one confirming that where the quality and quantity of the works are shown on drawings and specification, the drawn information, i.e. the drawings, are the dominant document for *quantity* and take precedence over the specification, which is the dominant document for the *quality* of the workmanship and materials. If such a statement were included in the contract this would satisfy the legal requirements and would clarify the unstated convention which has existed within the industry for many years.

Progress payments (clause 4.2)

Whereas MW 68 provided for interim payments at four-weekly intervals only if the contract period exceeded two months, MW 80, in view of its possible wider application for larger contracts, has omitted this proviso, so that the architect has now to certify progress payments, if so requested by the contractor, at not less than four-weekly intervals on all contracts.

The reason for the change in description from interim payments in MW 68 to progress payments in MW 80 is obscure but possibly is intended to encourage the use of stage, as distinct from periodic, payments as provided for in JCT 80 and the 1981 JCT Design and Build Form.

It is surprising that more use is not made of this option as it would be a far greater encouragement to a contractor to get on with the work if he were only paid when he had completed it to a certain stage e.g. plate level, than the more common system of paying him regularly each month.

Work properly executed

MW 68 required payments to be made in respect of the value of the works which the contractor had completed to date, including those covered by variations, PC and provisional sums. MW 80 has, however, inserted the adjective 'properly'. While this does not relieve the contractor of his obligations under clause 1.1 to carry out and complete the work in accordance with the contract documents, and in no way places the architect under any obligations to the contractor to ensure that he does so, it does enable the architect to deduct from his certificate the value of work which in his opinion has been *improperly* executed. It would clearly be inequitable for an employer to have to pay for work which he had been advised was not to the required standard and the architect would certainly be held liable for negligence to the employer if he did so.

Interim certificates are, however, continuing valuations and if defective work, included and paid for in an earlier certificate, is subsequently discovered, the architect is clearly under a duty to deduct it from the subsequent ones.

The correction of work improperly executed

MW 80 has no specific provisions for the architect to issue instructions for the removal of work not in accordance with the contract, as in clause 8.4 of JCT 80, so the problems which occurred in the case of *Holland, Hannen and Cubitt (Northern) Ltd* v. *WHTSO* (1981) will not arise.

In that case hospital windows, installed by the nominated sub-contractor, let in water as a result of defects in design and workmanship. However since the architects did not specifically issue an instruction under JCT 63 clause 6(4) requiring their removal, Judge Newey held that the architect's agreement to the sub-contractor's proposed remedial work was not a valid notice under 6(4), and that the architects ought to have issued a variation instruction to the main contractors under clause 3(4) detailing changes required to overcome the design failures. As a consequence the employer had to pay the sub-contractor for the windows provided and the architects were liable to the employer for breach of contract and tort.

However, if the architect becomes aware that any of the work does not comply with the contract documents or conditions, he clearly has a duty to the employer and has power to issue the necessary instructions to the contractor for its removal and proper replacement under clause 1.1. In the event of non-compliance by the contractor he can order that the work be carried out by others under clause 3.5.

Stage payments

It is a matter of regret that the words 'subject to any agreement between the parties as to stage payments', as in clause 30(2) of JCT 63 and clause 30.2 of JCT 80, have not been included, since there are many instances when the interests of the employer would be better served by the contractor having the incentive of being paid only when he had completed a certain stage of the work, rather than being paid for as much or as little as he had accomplished over the past month. It should also be noted that by use of the words 'not less than four weeks' the option exists for the issue of certificates at calendar monthly intervals without amendment to the conditions or completion of an Appendix should this be more convenient to the parties, as it usually is, and provided it is so stated in the tender documents.

Unfixed materials

MW 80 provides (as does JCT 63 clause 30(2) and JCT 80 clause 30.2.1) for unfixed materials and goods delivered to or adjacent to the works to be included in interim certificates, provided that they are reasonably, properly and not prematurely brought on to the site and provided they are adequately protected. The architect in this instance has no option: he *shall*, if requested by the contractor, include their value (an option in JCT 80 which, in the opinion of one distinguished architect member of the Tribunal, could only be exercised coincidental with his letter of resignation from the practice). This, however, raises the question of the ownership of unfixed materials delivered to site and included in interim certificates.

In the past one had sympathy for contractors who, in a climate of broken promises and delays by sub-contractors and suppliers, wished to ensure the progress of the works by arranging for materials and goods to be delivered and stored on site, sometimes prematurely, since the main contractor remained responsible for their safe custody. However the *Romalpa* case (*Aluminium Industrie Vaassen* v. *Romalpa Aluminium* (1976), and more especially the case of *Dawber Williamson* v. *Humberside County Council* (1979), which concerned retention of title to unfixed materials on site which had been included in progress payments made by the employer to the main contractor, alerted the industry to the problems attached to this practice.

While architects and quantity surveyors had always thought that unfixed materials and goods included in interim certificates became the property of the employer, the legal position had in fact always been that if a sub-contractor brings materials on site, the materials remain his property until they are actually incorporated into the works. Only then does the title of the goods pass to the employer.

This was in spite of contractual provisions to the contrary e.g. in JCT 63 clause 13 and JCT 80 clause 15.

Since the sub-contractor is not a party to the main contract he cannot be bound in any way by provisions in the contract between the employer and the contractor that upon certification by the architect for unfixed materials and payment to the contractor the property shall pass to the employer.

This is made abundantly clear by the case of *Dawber Williamson* v. *Humberside County Council*. The plaintiffs were non-nominated sub-contractors under the NFBTE/FASS 'Blue Form', who brought on site 16 tons of Welsh slates to roof a school. Payment for these to the main contractor was included, as clause 30 of the JCT 63 contract required, in an interim certificate. This was paid by the employer to the main contractor but before he had remitted the monies to the sub-contractor, the main contractor went into liquidation.

The employer claimed that, since clause 13 of JCT 63 provided that the property in the unfixed goods should pass to the employer on payment of an interim certificate, the slates were their property. Humberside County Council therefore took them and fixed them to the roof of the school. They were then sued by Dawber Williamson for the tort of conversion, in that, it was claimed, the Council had converted the goods to their own use.

The court upheld the sub-contractor's claim for two reasons: Firstly, the sub-contractors were not parties to the contract between the employer and the main contractor and therefore were not in any way bound by the provisions of clause 13.

Moreover, under the standard contract there was no provision for the main contractor at any time to become the buyer or for the title to sub-contractors' goods to pass to him. Title in goods affixed to the building passed from the sub-contractor to the owner only when they were affixed.

As a result, the tiles were, and always remained, the property of Dawber Williamson and when Humberside County Council took them and used them for the roofing, they were guilty of the tort of conversion. In spite of the provisions of JCT 63 clause 13 no title to the goods could ever be passed to them by the main contractor, even though they had paid him for them. 'A man cannot give what he has not got' ... *nemo dat quod non habet.*

Architects can therefore be found guilty of negligence to the employer if they include in certificates unfixed materials to which the contractor has no title, and the only solution with regard to the latter may well be for them to include in their specifications a clause such as the following NBS standard clause:

'At the time of each valuation [the Contractor is to] disclose to the Architect [and Quantity Surveyor] which of the unfixed materials and goods on site are free from, and which are subject to, any reservation of title inconsistent with passing of property as required by clause ... of the Conditions of Contract, together with their respective values, when requested, and provide evidence of freedom from reservation of title.' (© NBS Services Ltd)

Or better still:

'The contractor warrants to the employer that, in respect of all unfixed materials on site for the said work which he has requested the architect to include in an interim certificate, he is the true owner thereof, free from any charges or encumbrances whatsoever, and he will transfer to the owner on payment of the certificate the title to the said materials.' (© John Parris)

Retention (clause 4.2)

MW 80, in clause 4.2, provides for 5 per cent retention (with space for the insertion of an alternative figure) to be deducted and retained by the employer from all progress payments. This provision for deduction from progress payments was not included in MW 68 prior to practical completion, presumably on account of the anticipated shorter contract period on the contracts for which the earlier form was intended. There is now also space for an alternative percentage to be inserted which allows the employer to ensure that an adequate amount has been retained to cover the cost of any defects which may become apparent, both during the progress of the works and during the defects liability period. On larger contracts a smaller percentage will be necessary and on smaller contracts a higher percentage.

While clause 30.5 of JCT 80 states that 'the employer's interest in the retention is fiduciary as trustee for the contractor and for the nominated sub-contractor (but without the obligation to invest)', and retention monies should therefore by law be set aside in a separate trust fund, in the present author's experience the requirement in clause 30.5.3 of the private edition for the employer to pay retention money into a separate fund is rarely if ever implemented. But the courts would no doubt treat funds in his hands that ought to have been so deposited as if they had been.

Not all retention money is, however, trust money and MW 80 does not contain this express requirement to hold the money in a fiduciary capacity as trustee.

In this contract therefore the contractor is not entitled to any interest, and in the event of the employer becoming insolvent, the retention monies would be his assets in the hands of a liquidator and the contractor will be relegated to the status of an unsecured creditor.

Previous payments

In addition to the deduction of retention from the value of work executed, the employer has also to deduct the amount of his previous payments during the progress of the works. JCT 63 and MW 68 contained the provision for the deduction from the value of certificates for progress payments the amount of previous *payments* made by the employer. This was clearly incorrect since the architect knew only of the amounts he had previously certified and should not be obliged to ascertain from the employer if his previous certificate had been paid or not. Future editions have corrected this to less amounts previously *certified* in the same way as they do in JCT 80 and the other standard forms.

Time for payment

MW 80 contains the obligation on the employer to pay to the contractor the amounts so certified within fourteen days of the date of the certificate. There is no procedure laid down in the conditions for the issue of this certificate (which is partly the reason for its admirable brevity) nor any details of when the date should be. Clearly, however, for consistency the procedure should follow that now in JCT 80, with the certificate issued to the employer and a copy to the contractor. Indeed the current standard RIBA forms have now been designed to be equally suitable for use unamended with MW 80 as with JCT 80.

In MW 80 there is no distinction, as there is in JCT 80 in clause 30.1 and 30.2, between the date of a certificate and the date of the issue of the certificate, but in view of the short timetable of fourteen days from the date of the certificate, and not of its receipt by the employer, architects are clearly under the obligation to send it to the employer on the same day it is dated. Similarly the employer is to honour it within fourteen days of that date, irrespective of the date on which he received it.

Penultimate certificates (clause 4.3)

Clause 10(i) of MW 68 provided that only if the contract period for completion of the works exceeded two months had the contractor the option to request interim payments. In MW 80, however, the contractor is entitled to request four-weekly progress payments on all contracts, however short the contract period. The provisions for payments due to the contractor on practical completion, which would otherwise have been his first and only payment other than that due on the final certificate, therefore become less important.

MW 68 clause 10(ii) provided that, subject to the contractor having supplied all the documentation reasonably necessary, the architect would within ten days of his certificate of practical completion, certify payment of 95% of the total amount due under the contract, including any necessary adjustments for PC and provisional sums, retaining the full 5% retention (none of which had been deducted under any previous certificates) until all defects had been made good at the end of the defects liability period three months later (or such other period as had been substituted) and the architect had certified accordingly.

In MW 80 clause 4.3 however, with the reversion to the more traditional progress payments from which retention is deducted, and the easier provision of longer defects liability periods, the arrangements have been changed to mirror those in the larger contracts with the architect having, within fourteen (instead of ten) days of the date of certification of practical completion, to issue a certificate for the balance of monies due on the full value of works executed to date, withholding only half the total retention previously withheld.

In practice of course it is often expedient for the architect to issue this certificate at the same time as the earlier certificate of practical completion due under clause 2.4.

While sidenotes to clauses are considered to be for convenience only and not legally binding on the parties, the retention of the word 'penultimate' would imply that the employer has no obligation to pay any other certificate before the final certificate. It would appear that this was an oversight on the part of the draughtsmen in view of the contrary provisions that have been specifically introduced by clause 30.1 in JCT 80 and which will presumably be corrected in MW 80 in due course.

Final certificate (clause 4.4)
In contrast to JCT 80, MW 80 clause 4.4 contains one of the few procedural requirements in the contract, in this case the timetable for the final valuation and certificate. Once a building has been occupied it would seem axiomatic that the builder would want to receive the balance of money due to him and the building owner a statement of the extent of his financial obligations as soon as possible. Sadly it is not always as simple as this. Architects may have difficulty in extracting the necessary financial evidence to substantiate a final valuation from contractors, their sub-contractors and suppliers, and contractors often have to persuade architects to leave their drawing boards, where they are preoccupied with their next job, to look at a final account which may well have been lying on their desk for the past several weeks, particularly if they know that it will contain evidence that will require them to issue a certificate to the employer for sums in excess of that which he has previously authorised.

Previously in MW 68 the clause simply laid down the same sequence of events and 'conditions precedent' as existed on the larger contracts, namely that as soon as the contractor had provided all the necessary information, the architect should issue the final certificate within ten days of his certificate of making good defects and the employer should pay within a further fourteen days.

MW 80 however now has the additional provision of a 'period of final valuation' placing an obligation on the contractor to provide this information within three months of practical completion or such other period as shall be inserted. This is usually, but not necessarily, the same as the defects liability period since, although it is clearly to everyone's advantage that the amount of the final valuation be known as soon as possible, the final certificate cannot be issued until the defect liability period has expired, all defective items made good and the architect has issued his certificate accordingly.

Improper pressures
The case of *Chambers* v. *Goldthorpe* (1901) established that an architect could not be sued for negligence in issuing a final certificate since he was acting as a quasi-arbitrator.

This position was, of course, overturned by *Sutcliffe* v. *Thackrah* in 1974. It is still, however, important to remember that, although paid by the employer, the architect must be completely impartial in the exercise of the duties entrusted to him and issue the necessary certificates which are due even when this does not accord with the wishes of the employer. This was quite clearly established by cases such as *Hickman* v. *Roberts* (1913) when an employer, because of his own financial difficulties, instructed an architect to withhold a certificate. The case confirmed that an architect has a duty to act impartially when issuing certificates.

More recently, in the case of *Hoenig* v. *Isaacs* (1952), when an employer refused to pay more than £400 on a £750 contract, on account of defects which cost only £55 18s 2d to put right, the architect's duty to act impartially was again confirmed.

It must also be remembered that, as the House of Lords said at the time of *Sutcliffe* v. *Thackrah*, while an architect must be fair and reasonable, he can, like all other professional men, be wrong without being negligent. An error of judgment is not the same as negligence.

While there have been a great many cases of architects being successfully sued for professional negligence there have never been any in the author's experience who has been successfully sued for an error of judgment.

The finality of the certificate
Once a certificate is issued contractors have no difficulty in recovering the monies due to them and this is equally true in the case of a final certificate.

However, at the same time many architects take the prudent precaution of obtaining a certificate from the contractor that he accepts the final valuation 'in full and final settlement' for the works executed.

Over-certification
Clause 4.4 ends with the requirement that the amount of the final certificate shall be a debt payable by the employer to the contractor or by the contractor to the employer, no doubt prudently included to cover any eventuality, but over-payment to the contractor should be a rare occurrence since there can be no greater example of negligence, at least in the eyes of the employer, than the architect who over-certifies.

Contributions, levies and tax changes
The sudden imposition of taxes and levies such as selective employment tax, the CITB levy and increased national insurance contributions could find contractors faced with a considerable increased financial burden which they were in no way able to pass on to the employer on fixed price contracts. Clause 31 was therefore amended in JCT 63 and lump sum fixed price contracts no longer existed truly as fixed price contracts, and became properly (but rarely) called 'limited fluctuation' contracts, whereby contractors were only responsible for increases in the costs of wages of the work people employed on the site and in the costs of materials. Any sudden changes in the contributions, levies or taxes imposed by the government were thereafter recoverable from the employer as was a further percentage, to be stated in the Appendix, to cover the increased cost of: labour in excess of the NJCBI rules and decisions, supervisory staff, plant, consumable stores, head office and depot overheads. For it was realised that contractors could not recover under the previous clauses the full amount of any increases in cost in these elements of their tender.

Changes in social security contributions, levies and/or taxes were restricted to those in respect of 'work people' which excluded site supervisory and head office staff, and adjustments in duties or taxes on materials only applied to those specifically listed.

It was considered that an addition to the payment to the contractor of increases in contributions, levies and taxes of the order of 20 per cent would result in the total recovery by the contractor of his increased costs on fluctuation contracts incorporating JCT 63 clause 31A, and 10 per cent would not be excessive on 'fixed price' contracts where the contract period did not exceed twelve months.

A similar option was therefore incorporated in MW 80 with the proviso that, should the contract period be of such a limited duration as to make such a provision inapplicable, it should be deleted; but since the original draft ran to four pages and the addition of such a provision would have destroyed the balance of the contract (as did the provisions for value added tax and the provisions of the statutory tax deduction scheme incorporated in the Finance No. 2 (1975) Act) it was incorporated by reference in clause 4.5 and in full in the Supplementary Memorandum.

Fixed price (clause 4.6)
It has traditionally been the practice in the building industry that all lump sum contracts of a duration of less than 12 months should be let on a fixed price basis. It was considered to be in the best interests of the employer in all sectors, government, local authority and private, that the contractor should allow in his tender, irrespective of the current rate of inflation, for all known and unknown increases in the price of labour and materials during the period of the contract.

This was not specifically stated in MW 68, but in view of the possibility of the use of MW 80 on larger contracts of a longer duration, it was thought advisable, notwithstanding the provisions for the recovery of government increases in contributions and taxes allowable under clause 4.4, to incorporate an additional clause 4.5 making it clear that under no account should any other changes (i.e. increases or decreases) be paid to the contractor.

It should also be noted that the increased costs even on a 52-week contract period entered between the commencement and completion dates in clause 2.1, which is extended under clause 2.2 by a variation ordered under clause 3.6, will not be recoverable by the contractor.

On those contracts where it is thought that clause 4.5 should apply and the contractor be allowed increases in contributions and taxes, he should either be allowed the actual increased costs in labour and materials, or those calculated under the Formula Rules – an alternative clause to 4.6 should be substituted.

Chapter 6

Statutory obligations

Whereas in Germany contractors are deemed to be competent to undertake the works described in the contract documents and to ensure that all materials and workmanship are in accordance with accepted standards of good practice, contractors in the UK do not seem to hold the same view and assume that they have no responsibility for design nor for providing anything other than that specifically shown on the contract drawings and in the specification.

This is, however, a fallacy and is not the view held by the courts. While the architect has an express duty to his client under contract to ensure that all necessary planning consents are obtained, that plans comply with the current building regulations, and to ensure that all charges due to the local authority are paid at that stage, the contractor has an overriding and absolute duty to comply with the law of the land and with its statutes, of which the Building Regulations are only one out of over 450 acts and 25 statutory instruments affecting the construction industry.

This duty was nowhere more clearly set out than in the case of *Townsend Ltd* v. *Cinema News* (1959) where it was held that the contractor was at fault in constructing two bathrooms containing toilets which were in accordance with the architect's design, but which he knew contravened the building regulations, compliance with which he was responsible for under clause 3 of the then current RIBA contract. The architect, who had told the contractor that he would issue the necessary notices to the local authority, was found to be liable in tort to the building contractor (John Parris, *The Standard Form of Building Contract*). These duties are equally clearly spelt out in the more recent case of *Street* v. *Sibbabridge Ltd* (1980) where even though the foundations to a garage had been built to a depth of 2 ft 9 in, as shown on the drawings, they were found to be inadequate and not complying with the building regulations.

It was subsequently stated in the judgment: 'The obligation to comply with the regulations is in terms absolute. The implied term to comply with the regulations must override any matter in the plans incorporated into the contract which it conflicts with.'

This was equally clearly spelt out in clause 3 of MW 68 and clause 5.1 of MW 80. What was obviously uppermost in the minds of the original draftsmen was the latter part of the sentence, requiring the contractor to pay all fees and charges in respect of the works. As contracts undertaken under MW 68 and 80 were unlikely to have builders' offices, stores and canteen on site for more than 18 months, these would not be rateable so that the only fees and charges then likely were those for the district surveyor's in the inner London area.

The various statutory instruments covering the Building (Prescribed Fees) Regulations 1982 enable local authorities to charge the cost of all visits by the building inspector, and this means that the clause is now likely to be relevant on all contracts, however small. One fee is due on the deposit of the plans and one on the commencement of work on site.

JCT 63 covered the consequences of the contractor finding such a divergence and placed the obligation on him, *if* he found any, to notify the architect in writing, and a similar sentence was included in MW 80 clause 5.1. The further provision in JCT 63 clause 4 and JCT 80 6.4.1 for the contractor to carry out such remedial work as was necessary and recover the cost from the employer as a variation was not included.

Both forms, however, now include the proviso that, subject to the obligation to notify the architect, the contractor shall not be liable to the employer if the works carried out in accordance with the contract documents or any subsequent architect's instruction do not comply with the statutory requirements.

Whether such an express provision can override the contractor's statutory duty, including that set out at the beginning of the clause, or in section 7 of the Unfair Contract Terms Act 1977, only the courts can decide. It is unlikely however to arise on a Minor Works private sector contract in view of the legal costs of such an action to establish a point of principle. Until this occurs the contractor is not relieved of his obligation to comply but the cost of his so doing must be borne by the employer which he in turn will no doubt be entitled to recover from his architect.

It should not be overlooked, however, that under the 1985 Building Regulations if the option of depositing full plans under Regulation 13 is chosen instead of giving notice under Regulation 12, and these plans are subsequently passed by the local authority, the local authority cannot subsequently require under section 36 that any work that they consider contravenes the regulations be taken down.

The local authority's own responsibilities in this connection have also been eased since the case of *The Peabody Donation Fund* v. *Sir Lindsay Parkinson & Co. Ltd* (1984) when Lord Keith, in an appeal to the House of Lords, said that the purpose of paragraph 15 in JCT 63 was:

> 'not to safeguard building developers against economic loss resulting from their failure to comply with the approved plans. It was to safeguard the occupiers of houses built in the local authority's area and also members of the public generally against dangers to their health which might arise from defective drainage installations.'

This was further reinforced by the decision of *D & F Estates* v. *The Church Commissioners* (1987) restricting liability for economic loss in tort solely in respect of physical damage, and by *Murphy* v. *Brentwood District Council* (1990).

Value Added Tax

The Finance Act which came into force in 1972 introduced the building industry in Britain for the first time to the complexities of Value Added Tax, a device of almost oriental cunning which at one stroke imposed on the man in the street the unenviable role of unpaid tax collector, with a new watchdog in the person of HM Customs and Excise, a department whose staff had hitherto no experience whatsoever in the complexities of the building industry and whose activities had previously been primarily concerned with the collection of import and excise taxes and the tax from returning tourists at the Channel ports and international airports in the UK. How else could a legal draughtsman have produced an act in which the employer was called a 'Contractor' and the contractor a 'sub-contractor'?

A great deal of effort was therefore necessary by the JCT on behalf of the professions, employers and building contractors during the latter part of 1971 and during 1972 to ensure that when the Act became law it was equitable and could be enforced with consistency by those responsible.

The tax was introduced under the Finance Act 1972, as amended and applied subsequently. The contract sum is stated as being exclusive of any Value Added Tax and the employer has to pay the contractor any Value Added Tax properly chargeable on the supply to the employer of any goods and services in the manner set out in the Supplemental Memorandum.

When VAT was first introduced all new work and alterations were zero-rated; only repairs and maintenance were charged at the standard rate. Certain work was 'exempt' but this only applied to services such as those in connection with hotel, accommodation, camping and fishing rights.

The principles were originally set out in a series of Customs and Excise Notices: 708 – The Construction Industry; 715 – Alterations, Repairs and Maintenance; and 719 dealing with refunds to which DIY house builders were entitled. On 1 June 1975 VAT Construction of Buildings No. 2 Order was issued, dealing specifically with the tax on civil engineering work in the grounds or garden of a private residence and excluding from zero-rating 'site restoration, clearing rubble, levelling the land, applying topsoil, laying grass and simple paths, planting trees or shrubs or elaborate ornamental works'.

While all new work and alterations were zero-rated and the tax on repairs and maintenance was only 8%, most contractors chose not to recover from the employer until the final account any VAT that had to be paid to HM Customs and Excise.

In June 1979 the standard rate of Value Added Tax for repairs and maintenance was increased from 8 to 15%, almost double that previously charged and now, at $17\frac{1}{2}$%, amounting to almost a sixth of the total cost of the work. A further Customs and Excise Note 716 was issued to simplify the transition and it reversed the previous Note which stated that the tax was applicable when the invoice was rendered, irrespective of when the work was carried out. The new rule made it possible for all work carried out prior to the date of change to be charged at the old rate and all that carried out subsequently to be charged at the new, irrespective of the date of invoice. This was intended also to facilitate any changes in the rate that might be made in the future.

While the tax on repairs and maintenance was only 8%, relatively few problems arose, the amount of tax involved rarely justifying the cost of an appeal against the ruling of a local Customs and Excise office, even if this proved inconsistent with those of another region. Between 1979 and 1984, however, because of the seemingly arbitrary distinctions between alterations and repairs in the many examples set out in Customs and Excise Note 15, a great number of appeals were made against the findings of the VAT Tribunals. A number of these were taken to the High Court, the Court of Appeal and even to the House of Lords. As a result, those previously grey areas were more clearly defined. The 100 or so cases confirmed that, to qualify for zero-rating, an alteration had to be permanent, substantial, structural and involve materials 'ordinarily installed by builders'.

Value Added Tax Act 1983
This Act came into force in October 1983 to consolidate earlier statutory

provisions. It included changes in the penalties for offences and gave additional powers to the Commissioners to assess tax due on personal representatives and trustees in bankruptcy. It also dealt with credit and tax allowable for input tax, zero-rating, exempt supplies and exemptions.

All this, however, became irrelevant when in the 1984 budget the Chancellor announced that, with effect from the coming 1 June, all alterations and secondary buildings would be taxed at the standard rate.

New buildings

The 1984 changes excluded from zero-rating certain 'secondary' buildings such as detached garages, greenhouses, garden sheds and similar buildings in the grounds or garden of private residencies. These were to be standard rated. But it did not apply to commercial or industrial premises, in the unlikely event of anyone wanting to build greenhouses or garden sheds in the grounds or gardens of commercial or industrial premises.

Fitted furniture

From the outset HM Customs and Excise had sought to differentiate between different kinds of 'builders' hardware etc. in dwellings of a kind ordinarily installed by builders as fixtures', some of which were zero-rated and some not. The original Note 708 went into great detail, 'Fitted cupboards, work surfaces and sink units in kitchens, cupboards constructed across a recess or alcove in any part of the house' being zero-rated (para. 12), whereas 'units of fitted or built in cupboards (such as wardrobes, dressing tables and wall units)' were taxed at the standard rate (para. 13). This was confirmed by the appeals in two cases in 1982: *Smitmit Design Centre* v. *The Commissioners* and *Sharps Bedroom Design Ltd* v. *The Commissioners*. There it was held that, although the units did not extend the full width from wall to wall, nor did they have backs, both failed the 'structural' and permanence tests. Subsequently the 1984 changes established that fitted cupboards could be zero-rated but cookers, ovens, hobs, fridges, freezers, washing and dishwashing machines should still be supplied at the standard rate.

Work to existing buildings

The most radical change in 1984 was, however, the removal of 'alterations' from the classes of work that were zero-rated. From then on, whether the work constituted 'improvements, reconstruction, enlargement, repair, renovation or alterations' all was to be rated at the full standard rate of 15% which was by then current on both labour and materials. All home extensions, fitted kitchens, loft conversions, double glazing and central heating installations became liable for tax. The transitional arrangements were covered by taxing only that part of the work carried out after 1 June 1984 in a similar way to that when the tax was increased from 8% to 15% five years previously in June 1979.

On a larger project therefore, under the new VAT rules, it might well be more economical to demolish and rebuild as new an older building, than to attempt to renovate or alter it, since the 15% tax could by that means be avoided. In addition, a developer would be able to zero-rate the sale or long lease of the building which would otherwise have to be added to the list of their 'exempt' supplies.

The outcry that followed this proposal, when the consequences were fully understood by those concerned, resulted in the unusual step of two concessions being allowed by the Treasury – one for alterations for the handicapped and the other for alterations (but still not repairs which had also been suggested) to listed buildings.

Alterations for the handicapped (VAT Leaflet 701/7/84 dated 1 May 1984)
Group 14 of Schedule 5 of the 1983 VAT Act provided for 'supply to a handicapped person of services of adapting goods to suit his condition' to be zero-rated but it was sometimes suggested that altering buildings did not constitute adapting 'goods'. Group 14 was therefore altered in May 1984 to include the cost of 'constructing ramps or widening doorways or passageways for the purpose of facilitating entry or movement within a private residence' and for the 'supply of a service to a charity to enable this to be done to any building'. This was to include providing a bathroom, washroom or lavatory for the first time on the ground floor of the person's private residence.

This rather restricting and parsimonious concession was further relaxed in September 1984 by the addition of the words 'extending or adapting' the bathroom of a handicapped person and deleting the reference 'for the first time on the ground floor', thereby providing the flexibility of meeting the differing individual needs of people suffering a variety of handicaps.

Reconstruction (Protected Buildings VAT Leaflet 708/1/84 dated 1 September 1984)
After 1 June 1984 the only zero-rated services to building and civil engineering work were 'construction' and 'demolition', 'reconstruction' being specifically excluded. HM Customs and Excise did, however, concede that if only one wall of a building 'for example the front facade'

remained, a building making use of that single wall could be zero-rated. But if the remaining walls were also kept, 'even if the floors and roof had been removed', the work would have to be taxed at the full standard rate.

'Protected buildings'

A further relaxation was also achieved for work in connection with alterations to a 'protected' building. Alterations were defined as only that for those parts of the work for which listed building consent is required but still it specifically excluded 'repairs and maintenance'.

If repairs and maintenance were included in the application for listed building consent and were indicated on the drawings, the cost had to be identifiable and deducted from the sum qualifying for zero-rating.

'Protected' buildings were explicitly defined as those 'included in a statutory list of buildings of special architectural or historic interest' i.e. listed buildings. It did not cover unlisted buildings in conservation areas nor the now 'delisted' 'Grade III' buildings which are only considered to be of local interest. Buildings within the curtilage of a listed building were, however, considered to be included, as were scheduled monuments, alterations to churches if listed and currently in use, and buildings on Crown or Duchy land where listed building consent would have had to be obtained had they not been so owned.

The exemption is normally considered to apply only to the external walls and features such as roofs, domes, colonnades or entrance arches or architectural or historic interest. Internal alterations only qualify if listed building consent for the alterations is specifically required by the planning authority. This is always needed as evidence if the work is to be considered for zero-rating.

VAT Leaflet 708/1/85 stated that where contracts for 'protected' buildings include both alterations and repair, unless the cost of the work is apportioned, the whole is standard rated. However, this conflicts with the decision in *Sharman* v. *C & E Commissioners* (1983) where Judge Webster said that if the repairs or maintenance involved alterations, the whole should be zero-rated. There is therefore no authority for this statement by HM Customs and Excise, and as they withdrew their appeal when the 1984 changes were made, the opinion remains unconfirmed.

On at least one instance in the writer's experience an application for listed building consent for a private client was made solely in order to enable the alteration work to be zero-rated.

It is also necessary if the sale or granting of a long lease is to be zero-rated for the building to have been 'substantially reconstructed'. 'Substantial reconstruction' was originally thought to have to entail 50%

of the actual cost, but on 1 June 1984 it was increased to 75%, until it was reduced on 1 February 1985 to 60%.

All the foregoing is of great importance to developers involved in alterations and improvements, particularly those affecting listed buildings. Although zero-rating applies to the person constructing the building, reconstructed buildings, unless listed, no longer qualify. Its disposal becomes an exempt supply and this affects the amount of input tax the developer is able to recover. Unless developers are also involved in projects other than refurbishment contracts, they may be unable to register for VAT and are therefore unable to recover the tax.

VAT for Construction Industry (VAT Leaflet 708/2/87 dated 1 October 1987)

All the foregoing changes, other than those affecting handicapped persons and alterations to protected buildings, were consolidated in a new Customs and Excise Leaflet 708 in October 1987.

This confirmed that constructing a zero-rated building did not include converting, reconstructing, altering or enlarging an existing building, including:

- (i)   one where only the outer walls remain even without floor or roof
- (ii)   where internal features are retained in addition to any part of the external walls
- (iii) an additional flat on top of an existing block or a self-contained flat added on to a house.

It did however include:

- (i)   a building making use of part or all of the foundations of an existing building demolished to foundation level
- (ii)   a building using a single wall or two walls on a corner site
- (iii) building on to another house without interconnecting doors (*Perry* v. *Customs and Excise Commissioners* (1983)).
- (iv)   building a new house within an existing terrace
- (v)   each stage of a phased project within an initial planning consent.

Completion of construction

For the purpose of VAT, completion of a project is regarded as being the time of first occupation. Occupation of the ground floor before upper floors are fitted out, shop fitting, office partitioning and central heating in a new house before occupation are all zero-rated.

Garden buildings
Continuing their relentless pursuit of gardeners and DIY house builders, HM Customs and Excise made a new exclusion in 1984 of 'the construction of any detached building in the grounds or garden of a private residence from new buildings which would otherwise have been zero-rated'. The only exceptions were additional self-contained dwellings or detached garages or blocks of garages built at the same time as a new dwelling or a group of dwellings. It is therefore possible to build a zero-rated garage or house in a garden for one's widowed mother or chauffeur, but not a gazebo! Any other (subsequently built) detached garages and all other buildings, whether permanent or temporary, including 'surgeries, stables, greenhouses or garden sheds', are all standard rated.

Civil engineering
Similar principles differentiating *new* civil engineering work and civil engineering *reconstruction* follow those for building construction (new work having to be on new ground and sufficiently substantial to count in its own right). A long list of many examples is given in the Annexes to VAT Leaflet 708/2/85. Domestic civil engineering work in the grounds or garden of a private residence, such as a swimming pool, tennis court or formal garden, however is always standard rated, as is open cast mining!

Precise rules for civil engineering works, similar to those for the construction industry, were set out in VAT leaflet 708/3/85 dated 1 May 1985. However, few using the shorter forms of building contract are likely to be concerned with roads, bridges, sewers and water, defence work, airports and land drainage.

Separate supplies in new construction
Sixteen examples of zero-rated supplies and 12 to be taxed at the standard rate were set out as follows:

Zero-rated	*Standard rated*
site clearance	site investigation
earth moving	concrete testing
laying of foundations, brick	site security
laying, plastering, carpentry,	catering
roofing and plumbing	cleaning site huts
mechanical and electrical services	temporary lighting
plant hire	transport to site
scaffolding	plant hire

builders hardware (see Annexe II
and III)
kitchen units
builders' cleaning
first decorations
shop fitting
office partitions
vehicle crossings
remedial work
site restoration

scaffolding
professional services
construction management
landscaping

Building contracts

Fees for design and build, management contracting and construction management are standard or zero-rated, depending on whether this aspect is the responsibility of the contractor and is identifiable or not.

Specialist services

Sub-contracting, with a few exceptions, is zero-rated if the main contract work is zero-rated, e.g. new work. Otherwise it is standard rated. Complete demolitions are zero-rated, but not partial, which are standard rated.

Site restoration in the course of construction work, including the removal of rubble, levelling and drainage of land, application of top soil, laying of grass and constructing simple paths, are all zero-rated, but *not* transporting rubble from the site (if a separate service), landscaping, planting flowers, shrubs and trees, and the construction of fish ponds, rockeries and other ornamental works, which are always standard rated.

Plant hire is standard rated unless it includes an operator (but not a maintainer) and the work itself is zero-rated.

Scaffold hire is standard rated but not its erection or dismantling for zero-rated work. Domestic walls and fences, as one would expect, are only zero-rated when built in the course of the construction of a new dwelling or housing development.

Goods in new construction (zero-rated)

Just as in the case of services, most goods supplied in connection with new work are zero-rated, but some are specifically designated as being standard rated, such as fitted furniture, assembled, part assembled or made on site, and domestic appliances. Annexes II and III give a list of zero-rated examples. The main categories are:

Zero-rated goods	*Standard rated goods*
bricks and tiles	carpeting and underlay and tiles
glass	upholstery
pipes	curtains
timber	fitted furtniture and kitchens
sand cement	domestic gas and electrical
plaster	appliances
cables	trees, shrubs and flowers
wood	clocks, mirrors and blinds
space and water heating	TV aerials in dwellings
appliances	all free-standing equipment
re-usable fittings in show houses	goods to be used later
	builders merchants' goods

In short, all new work was zero-rated except garden buildings, 'domestic' civil engineering work (such as swimming pools and tennis courts), site restoration, formal gardens, landscaping services, planting trees, shrubs and flowers, fish ponds, rockeries and other ornamental works in the gardens or grounds of a private residence, all of which are standard rated.

Repairs and maintenance, alterations, fitted furniture, carpeting, curtains, and domestic electrical and gas appliances are also always standard rated, but alterations to listed buildings, kitchen units and work surfaces, space and water heating appliances are always zero-rated.

The supplier of the goods or service is always responsible in the first instance for deciding the VAT liability of the work carried out. Tenders, contracts and certificates always specifically exclude any VAT which the contractor may have to recover from the employer on goods or services which are not zero-rated. Contract conditions provide for the settlement of any disputes or appeals, should the employer wish to challenge the contractor's claims for reimbursement of any VAT liability due to HM Customs and Excise, and architects are often approached by their clients for advice in this connection.

VAT for Building and Civil Engineering (VAT Leaflet 708 dated 708/2/90)
The Finance Act 1989, amending schedule 3 of the 1983 Act, made virtually all building and civil engineering work except for domestic housing standard rated from 1 April 1989. This continued the previous minutiae defining the meaning of the construction and completion of buildings and their contents and was further regulated by VAT Leaflet 708/2/90. This allowed to be zero-rated, in addition to self-contained ordinary houses, bungalows and flats and civil engineering works for

permanent caravan parks (excluding, of course, 'tennis courts, swimming pools and similar works'), nine categories of self-contained residential buildings such as old people's homes, and boarding school dormitories and the construction of buildings intended for non-business use by a charity. (It was suggested buildings for a museum charging a fee would be standard rated!)

The leaflet explained the introduction of a new zero-rated category of buildings for the use as a village, community, church or similar hall for social and recreational facilities, including cricket pavilion and changing rooms, with the inclusion of Annexe E of a suitable self-certification form, the standard rating of which had previously caused much hardship to village communities, and covered also sub-contractors and demolition contractors involved in such projects.

Annexe B covers the usual detailed list of zero-rated products in dwellings and non-business charity buildings (outside lights but not lamps) including mirrors and barres in ballet schools, organs and humidifying plant in churches.

Annexe C – Furniture which is standard rated (including bathroom cupboards, desks and chairs).

Annexe D – Domestic electrical and gas supplies which are standard rated when installed in dwellings or other qualifying residential buildings.

Thus for the 1990s VAT at the standard rate is now payable for all building work including fixtures and fittings except that for new residential, non-business charities and protected (listed) buildings.

Supplementary Memorandum: Part B incorporating Amendment MW 6 (April 1989)

The Supplementary Memorandum in MW 80 regarding VAT appears to be unsatisfactory in a number of respects. It requires the employer to pay the contractor 'upon receipt of the contractor's written provisional assessment' VAT alleged to be due under Clause 5.2 for all buildings other than residential and other protected buildings. The contractor has no interest in whether the VAT is correctly due or not and is therefore likely to include it wherever possible, particularly as it may be in his hands and earning interest for several months before he has to pay it over to the Commissioners. At that stage the employer is in the unfortunate position of having to pay, whether or not he agrees or is advised that VAT is in fact due.

Only when he gets a final statement after the certificate of making good defects under clause 2.5 – which may be years later – is the employer entitled to challenge the contractor's contention that VAT is due.

Further, even then, he is not entitled himself to appeal to the VAT Tribunal against the decision of the Commissioners. That has to be left to the contractor, who has no interest whatsoever as to the outcome; only 'on the final adjudication of an appeal' is the employer entitled to be refunded over-paid VAT.

An informed employer might be able to delete the VAT Supplement Agreement and preserve his right to dispute whether or not VAT is payable as demanded by the contractor at any stage.

As far as building contracts are concerned VAT is dealt with as in the supplement to JCT 63 and was incorporated into MW 68 by an additional clause 16, increasing the size of the document at a stroke from three and a half to four and a half pages. In MW 80 this section was incorporated by reference in clause 5.2, confirming that the contract sum was exclusive of VAT and that any tax properly recoverable from the employer and due to Customs and Excise should be levied in accordance with the procedures set out in the relevant part B of the Supplementary Memorandum.

These are a condensed version of the seventeen clauses and sub-clauses in JCT 80 and in MW 80 cover the various aspects step by step in nine clauses in a relatively more simple way:

B1 – VAT means the tax introduced by the Finance Act 1972 managed by HM Customs and Excise with an additional clause B1.1 incorporating the provision of self-certification by the contractor on zero-rated residential projects.

B2.1 – The contractor shall inform the employer of the provisional value of those items in interim certificates on which VAT is chargeable.

B2.2 – The employer works out the tax and pays it at the same time as the certificate.

B3.1 – The contractor sends the employer, as soon as he can after the certificate of making good defects, a final statement including VAT already received.

B3.2 – On receipt of the final statement the employer calculates and pays the contractor the balance of tax due within 28 days.

B3.3 – If the employer finds that there has been an overpayment of tax he notifies the contractor who refunds the balance in 28 days.

B4.1 – On receipt of any tax the contractor sends the employer an 'Authenticated Tax Receipt'.

B5.1 – VAT is to be calculated by the employer on the value certified before the deduction of any liquidated damages.

B5.2 – Any liquidated damages are to be disregarded in the contractor's written final statement.

B6.1 – If the employer disagrees with the final statement he can ask the contractor to refer the matter to HM Customs and Excise for a decision.

B6.2 – If the employer disagrees with the decision of HM Customs and Excise he can instruct the contractor to appeal if he meets the cost.

B6.3 – The balance shall be paid or refunded within 28 days of the date of the decision.

B7 – The contract arbitration provisions do not apply to VAT appeals.

B8 – The VAT due on any alteration in the value of the works arising from the decision of an arbitrator shall be adjusted accordingly.

B9 – The employer shall not have to make any further payments of VAT to the contractor until he shall have received such authenticated tax receipts on previous payments that he may need and the tax has been paid by the contractor.

B10 – The employer shall not be liable for any future payments after the final certificate unless the Commissioners consider an error has occurred.

The application in practice
It is important to note that in theory the architect is in no way involved in the application of the Act. The building contract sum is always exclusive of VAT as is the value of the work on which he calculates his fees. In page 3 of Notice No. 715 is the statement:

'It is the supplier (that is the builder, contractor, decorator or self-employed craftsman, as the case may be) who is responsible in the first instance for deciding the VAT liability of any particular piece of work that he carries out.'

Nowhere in the Supplementary Memorandum, apart from the reference to the issue of certificates by the architect, is he referred to since the obligations of the employer to reimburse the contractor for any VAT he has to pay HM Customs and Excise arising from the works is entirely a matter between the two of them, although the writer has had occasion to remind a contractor of the fact when he attempted to include VAT (properly due) in an application for an interim certificate. In practice, of course, the architect is often required to advise the employer on the procedures involved and on whether the individual items are properly taxable or not.

It may often occur that the contractor only informs the employer of the value, VAT rate and date of supply of those items on which he considers VAT to be recoverable and leaves it to the employer to calculate, total up and remit the tax due to the contractor rather than the contractor doing it for him. This derives from the technicalities of the tax provision and it relieves the contractor of his liability to pay the tax to Customs and Excise until he has actually received the tax from the employer. This would not be the case had he calculated it himself when his liability would have started from the date of his 'invoice'.

Although there are relatively small amounts of tax involved (with VAT at $17\frac{1}{2}$ per cent), in the author's experience contractors now claim the VAT due in interim certificates and no longer leave the collection of the VAT which they are entitled to recover from the employer until the final certificate.

Statutory tax deduction scheme
Similar provisions to those for Value Added Tax were required as a result of the statutory tax deduction scheme under the Finance (No. 2) Act 1975, as amended by the Finance Act 1980 the consequential Income Tax (Sub-contractors to the construction industry) Regulation 1975 (SI 1975 No. 1960) and the Income Tax (Construction Operations) Order 1980 No. 171.

The problems of the successful avoidance of tax by sub-contractors in the construction industry, particularly the self-employed labour-only 'lump' (which under other circumstances might have been evidence of a commendable ingenuity and initiative on the part of those involved) had been the concern of successive governments until the introduction of this legislation in 1975.

Of even greater Machiavellian ingenuity than the provisions for the collection of Value Added Tax, this placed the responsibility on the employer for ensuring that those self-employed divulged their true income to the tax authorities and obtained a 'certificate' (in appearance like a plastic credit card) to this effect. If they failed to do this, then the employer would be liable for the payment of the tax to HM Collector of Taxes himself, notwithstanding the fact that he would, in effect, be paying for the work twice having already paid the contractor in full.

The position was made worse by the Treasury officials' lack of understanding of the provisions and procedures of the building industry and their calling the employer the contractor, and the contractor a sub-contractor in drafting the regulations. An employer achieves the otherwise impossible task of again becoming a 'contractor' under the Act merely by employing 'builders' who in turn are known as 'sub-contractors'. However these complications did have the desired effect of concentrating the minds of the employers on the problem and the Tribunal therefore drafted a new clause 30B for JCT 63, now clause 31 in JCT 80, and this was incorporated as clause 17 in MW 68 and in turn as clause 5.3 in MW 80 incorporating by reference part C of the Supplementary Memorandum.

The application of the scheme and these provisions are fully explained in JCT Practice Note 22 and whereas the status of the employer as a 'contractor' is not stated in the Appendix, as it is in JCT 80, clause 5.3 of MW 80 states that if the employer is a 'contractor' the following provisions shall apply:

C.1 – Definitions – The regulation means the regulation, the contractor means the contractor, verification means verification!

C2.1 – The building contractor shall provide the employer twenty-one days before the first payment becomes due with evidence that deductions are unnecessary or informs him they are required.

C2.2 – The employer, if he is not satisfied, notifies the building contractor within fourteen days that he intends to deduct tax from all payment due and requests the contractor for details of the direct cost of the materials involved.

C3.1 – If the building contractor does not have the necessary evidence he should inform the employer as soon as he has it.

C3.2 – If the tax certificate expires before the final certificate, the contractor must provide evidence to the employer if deductions are to be made from the final payment or not.

C3.3 – The building contractor shall immediately inform the employer of the date of cancellation of any certificate.

C4 – The employer must send the Inland Revenue any 'vouchers' which he receives from the building contractor.

C5.1 – The building contractor must provide the employer with details of the cost of all materials included in any certificate within seven days of the employer notifying him that he intends to make a tax deduction.

C5.2 – The building contractor must indemnify the employer in respect of any error in the details of the direct costs he has supplied.

C5.3 – If the building contractor does not provide details of the direct costs the employer shall make a fair estimate of them.

C6 – The employer shall correct any error in calculating or making the statutory deduction unless this conflicts with his statutory obligation.

C7 – Compliance with the Finance No. 2 Act Regulations overrides any other contract provisions.

C8 – Article 4 relating to arbitration between the employer and building contractor shall apply except where there is conflict with the Act or any other statutory regulation with regard to disputes.

In practice all prudent employers, or architects acting on their behalf, ask building contractors for photocopies of their current certificates prior to entering into the contract to establish the necessary future procedures and to note the renewal (expiry) date of the certificate. This is particularly important on Minor Works contracts which often involve the smaller contractor and sub-contractor, and prudent employers need to be meticulous in this respect if they are not to be held responsible for the tax of the firms or individuals they employ.

Fair wages resolution (clause 5.4)
Clause 5.4 was included, as in JCT 63 and 80, in order to ensure

compliance with local authority standing orders and therefore acceptance of MW 80 for local authority contracts. It was marked to be deleted if the employer was not a local authority but in practice it was often retained in private sector contracts also.

The Fair Wages Resolution was rescinded by Parliament in 1982 and the JCT deleted it, and the relevant part of the Supplementary Memorandum, from the contract by Amendment 5, in July 1988, clause 5.4 now being marked 'not used'.

Prevention of corruption (clause 5.5)

Provisions for the prevention of corruption were incorporated in the February 1977 revision of MW 68, as required by the Prevention of Corruption Acts 1889 to 1916 and sub-section (2) of section 117 of the Local Government Act 1972 with regard to the offering of any fee or reward to local government employees.

Whereas in JCT 63 and 80 such an act is a ground for determination by the employer under clauses 25(3) and 27.3, which includes the words 'whether with or without the knowledge of the contractor' to comply with the Ministry of Health Model Standing Orders this is not so included in MW 80. On the other hand clause 5.5. provides for the employer to 'cancel' the contract and in addition to recover from the contractor any loss which he the employer may have incurred as a consequence.

However, the clause, by using the additional words 'shall be entitled to' and not 'shall', allows the employer to decide whether or not to cancel and does not require him to do so, nor do the JCT draftsmen seem to have considered it necessary to cover the reverse situation, i.e. the corruption of the contractor by a servant or agent of the building owner in the unlikely event of an architect or clerk of works offering to accept sub-standard workmanship and materials in return for some pecuniary favour or the provision of labour or materials in his own home, in spite of the fact that this situation has been reputed to have arisen on contracts let under other conditions of contract.

Chapter 7

Injury, damage and insurance

Building work, by its very nature, is likely to be dangerous and the risks of injury to people and damage to property are high. It is clearly essential that the responsibilities of the various parties involved in the works with regard to these aspects of the contract must be clearly defined, and where necessary insurance provisions must be incorporated to ensure that those involved have the resources necessary to meet their responsibilities should an accident for which they are liable occur.

The strict liability of a building contract to a third person in tort (a civil wrong exclusive of contract) was established in 1868 in the case of *Rylands* v. *Fletcher* when a sudden and entirely unforeseen quantity of water, stored in a newly constructed reservoir, penetrated old and disused mineshafts and then escaped in other mine-workings owned by a Mr Rylands. In spite of there having been no negligent act or omission for which Fletcher could be held responsible, and although he was entirely unaware of the existence of the disused shafts, he was still held to be responsible.

While the construction of reservoirs over disused mineshafts is hardly an everyday occurrence in the building industry, the principles established in this case still hold good today. Adjoining owners are protected in law from things which, if they 'escape', are likely to cause damage, and these include not only water but weeds, trees, chimney stacks, motor cars, fire, electricity, vermin and chemicals, even 'escaping' vibrations and caravan dwellers! There are certain defences such as lack of ownership, and taking reasonable precautions, but the need to prove negligence is not one of them, and the perpetrator of the nuisance does not have to be the owner of the land, i.e. he can be an 'occupier' such as a building contractor.

The liability is a strict one, as has been said, but the situation is somewhat complicated as a result of the Limitation Act 1963, the Civil

Liability (Contribution) Act 1978 and the current practice of the courts of apportioning liability for damage between the parties on a percentage basis, instead of the earlier practice of holding one or other of the parties solely responsible.

Employers and contractors will both wish to avoid accidents on site, but when they do occur the sums of money involved are often large and insurers may therefore be inclined to incur high legal costs in perusing the clauses in their building contracts and insurance policies in an attempt to persuade the courts that they, the insurers, are not liable. This no doubt gave rise to the remark by the editor of 4th edition of *Hudson* who commented on 'the need for the utmost precision in drafting indemnity and insurance clauses. In both it is essential to define with extreme care the exact risks to be guarded against.'

The seven lines in which these liabilities were covered in the 1909 contract are now clearly insufficient!

It is for this reason that the JCT clauses regarding insurance are highly complex and almost incomprehensible to the layman. They have however been drafted to satisfy the requirements of the Association of British Insurers (ABI), a group of the leading companies in the insurance market.

The risks from accidents that may arise on a building contract fall into three categories:

(1) Fundamental, i.e. war, nuclear pollution, sonic booms, etc.
(2) Pure and particular: injury to persons and property.
(3) Speculative: inclement weather, shortages, vandalism.

The second category can best be set out diagrammatically, as shown in Figure 3.

In lump sum building contracts these risks are usually fairly apportioned between the employer and contractor (see Figure 4).

JCT 63 and JCT 80 in its original version dealt with the obligation of the contractor to indemnify the employer against injury to persons and damage to property arising from his own negligence (other than the works) in clause 20 followed by a clause (21) requiring the contractor to take out the necessary insurance to ensure that he has sufficient financial resources to meet his obligations in the event of an accident, and a further clause (clause 22) covering insurance against damage to the works arising from certain specified perils (fire, flooding, storm, civil commotion etc.) unless due to the negligence of the employer.

MW 80 was, however, arranged differently with three clauses, the first

INJURY TO PERSONS	DAMAGE TO PROPERTY
ON SITE (a) To employees of the building owner. (b) To employees of the contractor.	To the works by fire, storm, flooding, etc.
OFF SITE To third parties.	By collapse, subsidence, etc. – i.e. any other damage to any other property.

Figure 3

covering the obligation of the contractor to indemnify and insure the employer against injury to or death of persons arising from carrying out the works (clause 6.1), against damage to property (clause 6.2) and 6.3 covering damage to the works. There was, however, no provision for insurance to cover damage to property other than the works for reasons other than that due to the negligence of the contractor.

In 1986 the insurances clauses in JCT 80 were revised to take into account recent changes in the insurance market, particularly those relating to 'all risks' insurance which was increasingly being taken out by contractors under 'blanket' policies unrelated to any particular contract.

The Tribunal however considered that the type of project for which MW 80 was intended, i.e. works not of a complex nature, and of a contract value of not more than £50,000, was unlikely to be carried out by contractors with 'all risks' insurance cover and the earlier provisions incorporated in JCT 80 against loss and damage by fire etc. (i.e. the same list of perils defined as clause 22 perils in JCT 80 or specified perils in the 1986 amendments) were still applicable and suitable. Much work was likely to entail extensions, alterations or repair when the employer would be likely to be responsible for insurance against damage to the works by fire, but would not normally have an 'all risks' insurance policy.

The relief of the employer of any obligation in respect of injury to, or death of persons and damage to property arising out of the works is covered by the obligation of the contractor in both cases to 'be liable for and indemnify' the employer against any expense.

However the contractor is relieved of liability in the case of injury or death arising from the negligence of the employer and is responsible only for damage to property arising from his own negligence.

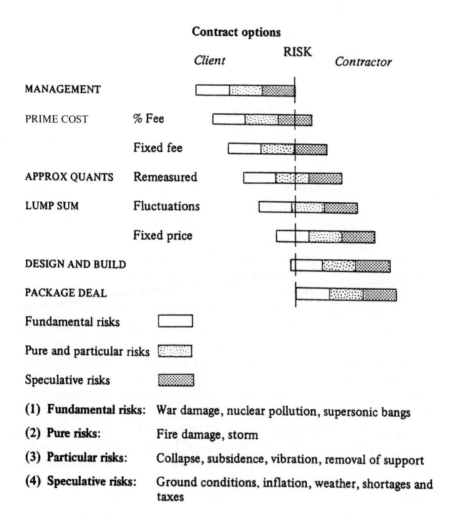

Contract options

| | Client | RISK | Contractor |

MANAGEMENT

PRIME COST   % Fee

Fixed fee

APPROX QUANTS   Remeasured

LUMP SUM   Fluctuations

Fixed price

DESIGN AND BUILD

PACKAGE DEAL

Fundamental risks

Pure and particular risks

Speculative risks

(1) **Fundamental risks:** War damage, nuclear pollution, supersonic bangs

(2) **Pure risks:** Fire damage, storm

(3) **Particular risks:** Collapse, subsidence, vibration, removal of support

(4) **Speculative risks:** Ground conditions, inflation, weather, shortages and taxes

Figure 4

Injury to or death of persons (clause 6.1)

The contractor's liability and indemnity to the employer is covered by the same words as are used in JCT 80 clause 20.1 and his liability for insurance in clause 21.1, with the exclusion of the liability of the contractor to insure in respect of negligence or breach of duty by the employer. The liability of sub-contractors is stated rather more concisely.

The reference to 'any statute' will include the Fatal Accidents Act and claims for loss of life expectancy. The words 'any person whomsoever' will ensure the inclusion of injury to third parties, probably not trespassers but possibly children for whom building sites have always held an irresistible attraction, and also of course authorised visitors such as the architect. The adoption of the words any person 'for whom the Employer is responsible' covers such visitors in addition to employees of the building owner, together with any 'Artists and Tradesmen' under direct contracts.

The contractor's liability and indemnity to the employer against injury or death of any person are absolute, and the obligation for the contractor to insure against such an eventuality arises from the need to ensure that, in the event of such an accident, he has sufficient financial resources to meet his legal obligations. The 1986 JCT insurance revisions strengthen the indemnity given to the employer by the additions of the words 'except that the same is' due to any act or neglect of the employer, and by the contractor and any sub-contractor being required to 'take out and' maintain insurance.

The specific requirement on the contractor to insure against his liability to employees and apprentices under the Employers Liability (Compulsory Insurance) Act 1969 was also incorporated in the 1986 insurance accidents. At the same time the last eight lines referring to injury, death and the exclusion of liability in respect of negligence or breach of duty of the employer, contractor, sub-contractors, servants or agents were deleted.

The responsibility of the contractor may, of course, extend long after the completion of the work since the clause refers to 'claims' and the effect of the 'loss' may only arise when a judgment has been made against him.

Damage to property (clause 6.2)

As far as damage to property is concerned, the contractor's liability only extends to claims arising from his own negligence, omission or default and merely covers damage to any property beyond the site boundary due to his own negligence. There is no insurance provision for damage arising from the negligence of the employer.

While the terms of insurance under clause 19(2)(a) of JCT 63 (JCT 80 clause 21.2.1) were such that claims under it were rarely made, and since the insurance is intended to cover unforeseen damage to adjoining property arising from unknown negligent acts of the employer, it is not surprising that the premiums subsquently quoted usually matched the provisional sums previously allowed.

There is no provision in MW 80 for the employer to take out his own 19(2)(a) insurance (as it is still called), the employer will either do this or arrange for insurances to be in the joint names of himself and the contractor, should the need for this protection be considered necessary.

In MW 68 clause 7(ii) there was provision for the amount of damage to property, real or personal, to be limited to £50,000 for any one occurrence or such other sum as was inserted. In MW 80 as first issued, this was deleted, the requirement being for cover for 'any damage whatsoever real or personal'. Where employers were in doubt that the contractor had sufficient insurance for a particular project, this could be remedied by the powers under the later clause 6.4 requiring the contractor to produce evidence that sufficient insurance cover is provided.

The clause was redrafted in the 1986 insurance revisions to make it clear that reference to property did not include the Works, adding the reference to 'injury' to property in the heading and in the text, together with 'breach of statutory duty' and the contractor's 'servants or agents, persons employed or engaged by the contractor upon or in connection with the Works or any part thereof his servants or agents'. This seems a rather long way of saying 'any person for whom the Contractor is responsible or any sub-contractor or person for whom the sub-contractor is responsible' – the phase used in the previous clause. But if, as a result, an insurer cannot escape liability which he would otherwise have been able to do, then it is presumably a small price to pay.

The most important 1986 change in this clause was the reinstatement of the provision for the insertion of a minimum amount of cover required. In the opinion of this author this is a retrograde step, since many employers or their advisers may be unaware of the correct amount to insert or, even worse, may leave the amount blank. When used for local authority projects, of course, no difficulties will arise, but for private sector projects a figure of less than £5,000,000 will rarely suffice.

Should the damage to the Works arise from one of the risks enumerated in the following clause, then of course it will have been covered by insurance taken out by either the contractor or the employer.

Insurance of the works – fire, etc: new work (clause 6.3A)

The departure from decimal numbering in clause 6.3A in MW 80 is deliberate and the affix A or B, given to those clauses with alternative provisions, is a reminder that one or other requires deletion (though for consistency this lettering system should also have applied to clauses 4.5, 5.4 and 5.5 where the option of deletion also exists).

MW 68 assumed that the work would almost always be within existing structures and therefore made no provision for insurance of the works by the contractor as was usual in the case of new work.

Since MW 80 was intended for a wider range of contracts it introduced, as an option, clause 6.3A requiring the contractor in the joint name of the contractor and the employer to insure the works against damage by fire, etc. on terms similar to those in JCT 63 and 80, but without the detailed requirements for the period of the insurance, the choice of insurers and the procedure in the event of the contractor having a policy already in existence – these being implied in the overall responsibility and the opportunity for the employer to inspect.

The insurance is to be in the 'joint' names which means that if the contractor already has a policy in existence the employer's interest in this particular contract must be endorsed on it to cover the interest of both parties in the event of a claim. The insurance has to be for the 'full value' of the works to ensure that not only does the insurance rise progressively throughout the progress of the works, reaching its climax with the full contract sum at practical completion, but the cost of removal and reinstatement in the event of accidental damage to the works are covered at current prices regardless of inflation.

The provision for an appropriate insertion for the necessary professional fees will cover the additional services of the architect, but not any consequential loss to the employer arising from the delay in completion.

The exclusion of temporary buildings, plant, tools and equipment owned or hired assumes that these are the responsibility of the contractor and sub-contractors as part of their normal business expenditure, as are the risks of damage arising from theft and vandalism which are also excluded.

While the JCT considered that the obligation for the contractor to take out cover for 'all risks' insurance on new work would cause unwarranted complications, the existence of such cover was not ruled out and a footnote to the clause was added in the 1986 amendments pointing out that, should such policies exist, they could be accepted, provided the policy was maintained and endorsed as recognising the employer as joint insured. The opportunity was also taken to ensure that the cover was for the full 'reinstatement' value and not just the cost of the works, to omit the exclusion of temporary buildings, plant tools and equipment owned or hired by the contractor, to permit the contractor to start rebuilding following a fire 'after inspection' required by the insurers in respect of a claim, and for the contractor to dispose of any debris. The reference to 'all' unfixed materials and goods intended for the works raises again the question of retention of title when for example the contractor did not have an insurable interest in the *Dawber Williamson* roof tiles and which makes the necessary declaration of title by the contractor even more important.

Once the claim has been accepted and the damage inspected by the insurers (not settled as in JCT 63), the contractor can make an earlier start in restoring the work, materials or goods damaged, remove the debris and proceed again with the completion of the works with any such extension of time as is appropriate.

There is no provision in this contract for determination if the period of delay exceeds one month, nor is it considered that this covers the delay if the employer suspends the carrying out of the works.

The contractor is obliged to complete the works at no extra cost to the employer regardless of any difference between the amount he receives from the insurance company and the actual cost to himself. He is reimbursed by certificates from the architect in the normal way, except that in practice those affecting the reinstatement works may be sent direct by the insurance company to the contractor and not to the employer if the money is paid in instalments as an alternative to a lump sum paid into a special fund.

Insurance of the works – fire, etc: existing structures (clause 6.3B)

The need for the employer to insure the works against damage by fire, etc. in the case of alterations, extensions and repairs to existing buildings is obvious: cover will almost certainly be required for damage to property other than that included in the works and the risks assumed by the employer are normally covered under his existing policies. All that is then required is for him to notify his insurers and rarely if ever is any additional premium involved other than that necessary to cover the increase in value of the property as a result of the 'works'.

For alteration work MW 80 follows clause 22.Cl of JCT 80 incorporating the words 'together with the contents thereof' to give full cover to the employer in the event of fire. But again there is no specific provision for consequential loss although most employers will have cover for this also.

The clause also ends with the same obligation on the employer 'to maintain adequate insurance against that risk' which is better than the earlier 'maintain a proper policy of insurance'. The contractor is properly given no right to object to the insurance company other than his right of inspection in the clause which follows in view of his obvious financial interest in the matter and the danger of the claim being 'averaged' if the property is under-insured.

Neither MW 68 nor MW 80 give the contractor the option of determination in the event of damage to the works such as exists in JCT 63 and 80, and the architect is empowered to issue such instructions for reinstatement as are appropriate under clause 3.5. These will be valued and paid for as any other variations under clause 3.6. If there is any shortfall in the amount recovered from his insurers this will have to be borne by the employer from his own resources.

Clause 6.3B for existing structures was also redrafted in 1986 and, as a consequence, now echoes more closely the phrases in clause 6.3A but makes no significant changes of principle, other than the reference to the valuation of the cost of any unfixed materials or goods under clause 3.6, omitting any reference to 'sole risk' and requiring the employer to insure under a joint names policy instead.

Evidence of insurance

As with JCT 63 and 80 in clauses 21.1 and 22.A2, the employer has the right to evidence from the contractor that he maintains or has taken out the necessary insurance to cover his liabilities under the contract. There is, however, no specific provision for the furnishing of a certificate of insurance, nor for approval of the company concerned, either when the insurance is taken out by the contractor or when it is taken out by the employer. Nor is there any provision for payment of the premiums by the other in default of the party responsible.

The provision of a certificate of insurance is preferable as far as the employer (or architect on his behalf) is concerned, since should it be subsequently found that the policies were in any way inadequate the production of the policies themselves could imply that their actual content had been approved by the architect, which few are competent to do.

Many local authorities are, of course, in a different position with a department specialising in insurance, as are many clients on larger contracts. They have insurance brokers knowledgeable in these matters and this clause gives them the right to inspect the policies themselves as the reasonable evidence to which they are entitled. They may well feel this to be necessary in view of the omission of the upper limit of insurance against damage to property previously to be inserted in clause 6.2.

Many private employers, however, will be unaware of the maximum amount of cover required and it is clearly therefore in their best interests to take advice to ensure that the contractor's insurance is sufficient to cover any expense, liability, loss or claim in proceedings.

In MW 80 because of the additional clause making the contractor responsible for insurance in the case of new works, a similar obligation on the employer to produce the necessary evidence has been added.

The words 'taken out and in force at all material times' are quite clear and safeguard the rights of the parties in ensuring that the necessary insurance exists.

In the case of *William Tomkinson* v. *St Michael PCC* (1991) referred to earlier, Judge Stannard held that:

(1) clause 6.3 is concerned only with violent and unusual perils
(2) a heavy downfall of rain did not necessarily have these characteristics
(3) the contractor was therefore responsible for damage by rain to the property of the employer elsewhere on the site
(4) the architect had an obligation to advise the employer to have the necessary insurance when clause 6.3B applies.

Chapter 8

Determination

While the clauses and grounds for determination in the JCT contracts, including MW 80, look comparatively simple, they are fraught with hidden dangers. Legal advice, in the event of it being thought necessary to determine a contract, is essential.

The first essential is to ensure that the contract is properly determined and not repudiated by one side or the other. 'Repudiation' occurs when it becomes clear that one or both of the parties to the contract cannot or will not complete that which they had set out to do, and either by expressly saying so or by their conduct indicate beyond all reasonable doubt that they no longer intend to be bound by the contract.

It is essential that the legal formalities of determination are followed exactly, since the first point the lawyers in any subsequent litigation will attempt to establish is that the contract was wrongly determined, even on a technicality such as arose in the case of the *London Borough of Hounslow* v. *Twickenham Garden Developments* (1971) when the contractor refused to vacate the site; in *Sutcliffe* v. *Chippendale and Edmonson* (1971) when the issue was the determination of a contract between an architect and his client; or in *Holland, Hannen & Cubitt* v. *Welsh Health Technical Services Organisation* (1981) concerning defective windows. In each case it was held to be essential that the contractor's attention be drawn to what was wrong, that he be instructed to put it right within a specified period and be informed of the consequences should he not do so. The employer must 'serve' this notice, and not the architect, as in JCT 63 and 80, and it is clearly essential that he should have meticulous and informed legal advice in its drafting and delivery if the case is not to be lost on a technicality.

Determination by the employer (clause 7.1)

The disadvantageous position of the employer with regard to determination which exists in JCT 63 and 80 is not, however, repeated in MW 80 – which is perhaps yet another reason for its wider use.

The employer *may* – 'but not unreasonably and vexatiously' – determine the employment of the contractor. The meaning of these words is now no longer in doubt having been defined in *Hill* v. *LB of Camden* (1980) when it was made clear that serious damage must have arisen and that the contract could not be determined on such a technicality as a certificate being a day late. In the same case the notice was delivered by hand whereas the contract specifically requires it to be delivered by 'registered post or recorded delivery' and as was pointed out it is essential to establish the date and time of its service since the notice only operates from the time it is received.

MW 80 follows MW 68 with the exception of the omission of the words 'that is to say' one or more of the following respects, which is not material and was omitted presumably as being superfluous. It does not require any warning to be given to the contractor, the notice 'forthwith' determining his employment.

The employer has two grounds on which he may determine the contract: firstly if, without reasonable cause, the contractor fails to proceed diligently or wholly suspends the carrying out of the works.

This may be a very difficult question of fact to establish legally, particularly if, in the absence of a contractual requirement for a progress schedule, none has been provided and reliance has to be placed on the court looking at the picture as a whole and taking a broad view having no doubt listened to the conflicting expert opinions presented by each side. Sir Derek Walker-Smith, in *The Standard Form of Building Contract*, has suggested that 'it merely stresses what would otherwise be an implied term of the contract [JCT 63] namely that the Contractor should show that degree of despatch and exertion which would be reasonably expected of him'.

The employer's second ground for determination is if the contractor has 'wholly' suspended the work. It is difficult to establish what is 'partially' suspended and what is the difference between 'wholly suspended' and 'stopped' and whether 'suspend' eliminates the essential quality for repudiation or refusal to go on and introduces a temporary quality into the word 'stop'. This is clearly an exercise which the legal profession would enjoy, and has enjoyed spending many hours in attempting to define. Clearly, therefore, very careful consideration of the position is essential before determining the contract on these grounds.

The retention in MW 68 and 80 of the reference to determination of the *employment of the contractor*, as in JCT 63 and 80, and not determination of the *contract* is equally important.

The judgment in *Sutcliffe* v. *Chippendale and Edmonson* (1971), quoted by John Parris (*The Standard Form of Building Contract*), on the question of the employer's right to determine the employment of a contractor gives much needed guidance.

'The whole combination of circumstance ... did justify the plaintiff in ordering the contractors off the site. Their manifest inability to comply with the completion date requirements, the nature and number of complaints from sub-contractors and the admission that in May and June the quality of work was deteriorating and the number of defects multiplying all point to the plaintiff's expressed view that the contractors had neither the ability, competence nor the will to complete the work in the manner required by the contract. Accordingly I find the plaintiff was justified in determining the contract.'

On contracts where similar circumstances arise then clause 7.1 empowers the employer to determine accordingly.

Financial failure of the contractor

The only other option permitting the employer to determine (and it is an option and not automatic as in JCT 63 and 80) is if the contractor:

  (i)   becomes bankrupt
  (ii) makes an arrangement with his creditors
  (iii) has a winding up order made or voluntary resolution passed
  (iv) has a receiver or manager appointed
  (v)   has possession taken of any property which is the subject of a charge.

In this case, these being matters of fact, no difficulty should be found in establishing their existence but there is no obligation on the employer to determine. Nor is there any obligation on a receiver or a liquidator to determine and it is often in the employer's interest to persuade those involved to allow for the work to continue under whatever arrangements are considered appropriate or at least for all agreements for the supply of goods to be assigned.

The employer's repossession of the site (clause 7.1)

MW 80 clause 7.1 also includes a new provision obliging the contractor, in the event of a proper determination, to give up possession immediately and relieves the employer of any obligation to make any further payment to the contractor until completion of the works: two valuable provisions which are rightly in the employer's interest and which follow JCT 80 in dealing with the problem raised in *LB of Hounslow* v. *Twickenham Garden Developments* (1971) where the contractor refused to leave the site, and was held to be entitled so to do.

Unlike JCT 80, MW 80 is silent on the other financial consequences of determination and on the use by the employer of unfixed materials, temporary buildings, plant and equipment on site.

The words 'without prejudice to any other rights or remedies which the Employer may possess' at the end of the clause have the effect of preserving the employer's rights at common law and if the contractor's conduct can be interpreted as repudiating the contract or breaching a fundamental condition the employer is entitled to treat the contract (not just the employment of the contractor) as at an end.

Determination by the contractor (clause 7.2)

Clause 7.2 of MW 80 starts with identical words to clause 7.1 and gives the contractor the option to determine his own employment. As in the case of the employer he may, though 'not unreasonably or vexatiously … by registered post or recorded delivery … forthwith determine' but for four not two reasons.

(1) Failure to receive progress payments within fourteen days of certification

It is important to note that there is no right to suspend the work in the event of certificates not being honoured by the due date. This point was considered by the Joint Contracts Tribunal at the request of the RIBA both for MW 80 and JCT 80, particularly as such a right exists for sub-contractors under NSC4 and DOM/1, but it was decided that this would not be in the contractor's interest in that it would give the employer an option to delay payment without invoking the drastic consequences of determination, and would not be in the contractor's best interests if his cash flow, on which his very existence often depends, could be capriciously interrupted in this way.

(2) Interference, obstruction or non-availability

An equivalent to MW 80 clause 7.2.2, which provides for determination by the contractor in the event of interference or obstruction by the employer or failure to make premises available, does not exist in JCT 80. Nor are there any safeguards to the contractor justifying an extension to the contract period in the event of failure of the employer to give in due time ingress or egress to the site.

(3) Notice of determination by the contractor

Whereas there is no provision for the employer to give the contractor prior notice of his intention to determine under clause 7.1, a new provision has been incorporated in clause 7.2 in MW 80 allowing the employer seven days from receipt (not issue) of the notice to make good any default in progress payment, interference or suspension of the works before the contractor can determine his employment.

(4) Payment to a contractor determining his employment

While the contractor is not entitled to any payment prior to the completion of the works if his employment is properly determined by the employer, the situation is different in the case of determination by the contractor.

Under these circumstances MW 80 has introduced a clause whereby the contractor is quite properly entitled to be paid a 'fair and reasonable sum' in respect of the balance due to him for the value of work begun and executed, materials on site and the removal of all temporary buildings, plant and tools. The clause is, however, silent as to when such sum shall be paid (possibly because a contractor cannot be a preferential creditor of a bankrupt employer); nor is the contractor entitled to payment for 'any direct loss/or damage' caused by determination, as he is under JCT 80 clause 28.2.6. This is clearly to the employer's advantage, particularly as he would otherwise be required to pay the contractor the profit he would have made had the contract been completed. This the contractor was able to do in the case of *Wraight Ltd* v. *P.H. & T. Holdings Ltd* (1968) when, after eight weeks on a 60-week contract for about £54,000 entered into in September 1964, the architect suspended the work because of unexpected soil conditions and the contractor left the site the following month and issued a notice terminating the contract under JCT 63 clause 26.

In a High Court judgment on a case stated in an award by an arbitrator Mr Justice Megaw, having said there was 'no grounds for giving the words direct loss and/or damage any other meaning', awarded the contractor £5,159, being the gross profit he would otherwise have expected to have made, had the contract been fulfilled.

The clause ends with the proviso that the right of determination is without prejudice to the contractor's rights, for the same reasons as the phrase is included in clause 7.1 covering determination by the employer.

Suspension by the employer

Unlike JCT 80 there are no specific grounds in MW 80 under which the contractor may determine if the employer suspends the works for reasons such as the seven itemised in clause 28.1 of JCT 80: *force majeure*, architect's instructions, civil commotion, etc.

The new clause 7.2.3 in MW 80 provides for *any* suspension for a continuous period of at least one month. In theory, therefore, an employer in financial difficulties could suspend the work for three weeks every month for a continuous period without giving the contractor legal grounds for determination. However this would probably be considered 'unreasonable' if not 'vexatious' and would also be inappropriate in a contract the conditions of which are based on the assumption of the parties behaving in a fair and reasonable manner.

Under clause 7 of MW 80 an employer *may* determine the contract if the contractor has a receiver appointed whereas under JCT 80, before Amendment 11 was issued, the contractor's employment was *automatically* determined on appointment of a receiver.

Financial failure of the employer

Whereas JCT 80 does not envisage the financial failure of a local authority employer, MW 80 makes no such distinction – perhaps wisely in view of the financial performance of some of the London Boroughs – and it includes in the grounds for determination by the contractor provision for the financial failure of the employer in almost identical terms to those covering the financial failure of the contractor.

The use of the word 'a' composition in place of 'any' composition, the omission of the proviso 'except for the purpose of reconstruction' (unless it is assumed local authorities cannot be wound up and reconstructed) before a resolution for voluntary winding up and the omission of a receiver or manager being 'duly' appointed as exists in the contractor's clause are not clear.

The Insolvency Act 1986

MW 80 was revised for the third time by Amendment MW 3 in August 1987 by the addition of 7 lines in clause 7.1.2 incorporating the additional reference to proposals for voluntary arrangements or schemes for the composition of debt under the Insolvency Act 1986 as grounds for the determination of the employment of the contractor by the employer.

A similar provision was made by the substitution of a new clause 7.2.4. adding proposals for voluntary arrangements (except those for the purpose of reconstruction), schemes for the composition of debts, or, if the employer has an administrative receiver appointed under the Insolvency Act 1986, as grounds for determination by the contractor.

Repudiation

In the case of *Alexander Corfield* v. *David Grant* (1992), a dispute between an architect and his client regarding fees for a hotel conversion, Judge Bowsher, sitting as Official Referee, held *inter alia* – having described the architect's performance as an 'inadequately controlled muddle':

'The plaintiff continually did or omitted things to such an extent that his conduct showed an intention not to perform the contract.

The effect of the breaches by the plaintiff was such that the defendant lost confidence in him and was entitled to accept his breaches as a repudiation of the contract.'

Chapter 9

Settlement of disputes – arbitration

In the original edition of MW 80 the arbitration clause was moved from the end of the conditions into the Articles as Article 4. In 1988 the JCT, by Amendment 5, added a new section 9 for the settlement of disputes by arbitration at the end of the Conditions, leaving only the reference to the appointment of the arbitrator in the Articles.

Ever since *Sutcliffe* v. *Thackrah* in 1974 established that an architect could not be considered a quasi-arbitrator in respect of certification, his only duty under the contract has been to act 'fairly and reasonably'.

If the contractor, when he receives a certificate, feels that the architect has acted otherwise (for example, he may consider his application for an extension to the contract period to have been 'unreasonably' rejected) he can then notify the architect accordingly, in a letter for example stating:

'Whereas disputes and differences have arisen between you and ourselves within the meaning of Article 4 of the Contract dated ...... between ...... and ...... I hereby give you notice of our intention to have such differences settled by arbitration in accordance with the conditions of the contract'.

Such a notice can be issued under MW 80 at any time either before or after practical completion and sets in train procedures usually on the following lines:

(1) The arbitrator sets up a 'preliminary' meeting between the parties to the dispute, or their solicitors, to agree a timetable for the exchange of 'pleadings' which set out the case for the claimant and defendant, for any further particulars of the supporting evidence which will subsequently be provided at the hearing, together with arrangements for its subsequent location, duration, date and time of commencement.

(2) At the hearing each side presents his case with supporting evidence, witnesses and experts. The JCT rules for arbitration, incorporated in the conditions, now provide for one of three procedures – written only arbitrations, oral only arbitrations, or the traditional full procedure which usually lasts for at least three or four days – for each side to present their case in as much detail as they think is necessary. When large amounts of money are involved, arbitrations under the full procedure are little different from disputes taken to the High Court.

(3) After the end of the hearing, the arbitrator draws up his award, giving his decision in writing, and directs which of the parties is to pay his own and the costs of the successful applicant.

The advantages of arbitration over litigation in the courts are often challenged by solicitors and lawyers and each case must be considered individually on its merits but it is generally accepted that:

(1) An arbitration hearing is private with only the parties to the dispute, their lawyers, witnesses and experts present.

(2) The time and place of the hearing can be arranged at relatively short notice to suit the convenience of those involved and not just the court.

(3) If the parties so wish, a decision can be arrived at more quickly and cheaply than through the courts.

(4) The person chosen as arbitrator will usually be conversant with the technical aspects of the problem.

(5) The award of the arbitrator is confidential and not made known to anyone other than the parties to the dispute unless leave is given to appeal it.

The *lex fori*, the law of the place where the arbitration takes place, will govern the procedure of the arbitration, irrespective of the place where the work was done.

It must be remembered that since the architect is not one of the parties to the contract, it is the employer and not the architect who becomes the claimant or respondent in the arbitration. This is particularly important as there is no provision in the Arbitration Acts for joining third parties as is provided for in both JCT 80 and in a High Court action brought under the procedures laid down in 1850 by which third parties can be brought into an action in order to indemnify either party to the dispute against any damage, loss or expense for which they may be considered to be responsible.

JCT 80 in Article 5.3 provided for the arbitrator to have power to 'open up, review and revise any certificates, opinion, decision, requirement or notice of the Architect'. This led the Court of Appeal in *Northern Regional Health Authority* v. *Derek Crouch* (1984) to decide that, although the arbitrator might have such powers, no court had, even though Official Referees had habitually exercised such power for many years. The Fourth Amendment to JCT 80, published in 1987, appears to remove such power from an arbitrator by making the architect's certificates regarding extensions of time and direct loss and expense claims (the most frequent type of dispute) 'conclusive evidence' unless the contractor has given notice to go to arbitration prior to practical completion.

MW 80 did not contain such words about the powers of an arbitrator. Judge David Smout QC sitting as an Official Referee in *Oram Builders Ltd* v. *M.J. Pemberton & Ano* (1985) decided that MW 80, Article 4, did not explicitly empower the arbitrator to open up and review the architect's certificates and that the courts had no power to do so either except in the event that an Official Referee was appointed to settle the matter as an arbitrator (as he could be) instead of in his usual capacity as a High Court judge.

The question as to whether an arbitrator appointed under MW 80 has power to reopen and review the architect's certificates also came before the Court of Appeal in *Crestar* v. *Carr and Ano.* (1987) when Lord Justice Fox held that the wording of the arbitration clause was wide enough to allow the architect's final certificate to be challenged.

The case concerned the alterations to a house in Essex carried out under MW 68, which were due for completion in February, but practical completion was not achieved until the following June. When the architect issued his final certificate in October for an outstanding balance of £40,000 (having previously issued interim certificates to a total of £70,000) his clients, Mr and Mrs Carr, tried to have the matter referred to arbitration. The contractor resisted on the grounds that clause 10 of the contract required the certificate to be honoured within 14 days, the amount being an 'uncontestable and non-arbitrational debt'. The court also held that an arbitration clause might continue to subsist for the purpose of determining whether the provision of the contract had been duly performed even though the contract itself might have come to an end. The judge said:

'The condition contains no limitation of time as to the reference of disputes to arbitration. Having regard to the width of the arbitration provision and the absence of any express provision as to the conclusiveness of certificates, I am not prepared to infer that the parties intend to prevent the owners referring matters to arbitration after the end of the 14 day period'.

The most recent case concerning the right to arbitration under a JCT Minor Works Form is that of *Chrisphine Othieno* v. *Mr & Mrs Cooper* (1991) relating to a builder who had carried out work under the supervision of an architect to the value of £81,870.33 in Trinity Road, Tooting. The dispute concerned the question of whether the works were 'practically complete', whether the employer could determine, the issue and payment of interim certificates, and defective or omitted work. The case was remitted to Mr Justice Garland sitting as judge in chambers to decide two issues:

(1) Whether, notwithstanding the existence of an arbitration clause in the contract, the dispute could be heard in the court, thereby allowing the claimant legal aid to which, being an individual (and not a company), he would not otherwise be entitled.
(2) Whether, in view of the decision in the *Crouch* case, if the dispute was referred to the court, the certificates or decisions of the architect could be reviewed or revised.

The judge, having stated rather surprisingly that the only other case involving judicial consideration of the Minor Works Form, as far as he was aware, was *Benstrete Construction Ltd* v. *Angus Hill* (1987) held that, in view of the financial difficulties of the claimant caused by the defendant's breach of contract, he should exercise his discretion and allow the case to proceed. The early decision on the JCT 63 *Crouch* case did not apply to the JCT Minor Works Form since as far as he could see the JCT MW form did not contain, in addition to a main arbitration clause, an internal arbitration clause such as existed in JCT 63 in the *Crouch* case. He saw no reason to distinguish the Minor Works Form from a host of other commercial contracts containing an arbitration clause and neither the plaintiff nor defendants would be in any way disadvantaged if the matter proceeded by way of litigation.

The 1988 JCT MW 5 revision to Article 4 and the provision of a new section 9, 'Settlement of Disputes' Arbitration, with five separate 'internal arbitration' clauses will presumably achieve the necessary precision and clarify once and for all the powers of an arbitrator under MW 80 to review certificates and decisions of the architect.

Disputes and differences (9.1)
Should any dispute or difference arise between the employer (or his architect) and the contractor as referred to in Article 4, either must give written notice to the other and unless they can agree within 14 days on a suitable individual as arbitrator, and they rarely can (each side thinking the choice of the other will have been selected as to give an unfair bias in favour of the proposer), then an arbitrator will be nominated for them by the President of the RIBA or RICS.

Power to review (9.2)
This clause gives the arbitrator the power, which it is argued a judge or Official Referee does not have, to open up, review and revise any certificates, opinions, decisions, requirement or notice of the architect. This provides the arbitrator with similar powers to those of a town planning inspector in regard to an appeal of an applicant against a refusal of consent or the imposition of unacceptable conditions.

Final and binding (clause 9.3)
The award of an arbitrator is final and binding, unless a dissatisfied party can obtain leave from the High Court to appeal under section 1 of the Arbitration Act 1979. An appeal will lie on 'any question of law' arising out of the award. Such leave will not be granted unless the determination of the question of law concerned would 'substantially affect the rights of one or more of the parties'. The statutory provisions have been restricted even further by decisions of the House of Lords which have held that leave should only be given where the point at issue is applicable to standard contracts and not to 'one-off' situations.

The death of an arbitrator (clause 9.4)
Unless the parties expressly agree otherwise, a second arbitrator appointed after the death of the one originally appointed has to start all over again. But it is obviously in the interests of the parties, and will save expense, that they agree that the second arbitrator will be bound by the decisions of the original one.

The JCT Arbitration Rules (clause 9.5)
The JCT published in 1988 a set of arbitration rules, some of which contained stricter obligatory time limits than those prescribed by other

Rules to be adopted if the parties agree

	Choice of rules	Discovery	Documents	Oral evidence	Timetable extensions	Security and award of costs
RULE 5	Applies unless parties want Rules 6 or 7	If required	Full but no discovery	Nil	Extensions by arbitrator limited	Awarded (and taxed) by arbitrator
RULE 6	Applies if the arbitrator decides or the parties so request	If required	Full with experts and full discovery	Full	Arbitrator shall dismiss or extend. Timetable in Rules – (not by arbitrator) 12–26 weeks = 6 months + hearing	Awarded (and taxed) by arbitrator
RULE 7	Only if requested by claimant and agreed to by respondent	Unlikely to be necessary	Few and additional written evidence discouraged	Full	4–6 weeks	Low. Not awarded (borne by parties)

(1) Arbitrator has power to dismiss through lack of prosecution by claimant.
(2) Joinder provisions available.
(3) Note this is only a summary. The JCT Arbitration Rules should be referred to for full details.

rules or to be found in practice. This was to meet the criticism that a dispute to be settled by arbitration can sometimes take as long as the normal litigation procedure. The JCT Rules included two options, in addition to the full procedure under Rule 6. Rule 5 provides for disputes to be settled on the basis of written evidence only, similar to that available in planning appeals, and Rule 7 provides for a procedure based on oral evidence only, supported by an agreed statement of facts. Both rules have been drafted with the stated aim of resolving a dispute within 30 days (while matters are fresh in the parties' minds), instead of the 30 months or so which are often required under the full arbitration procedures, or three years or more through the courts. For further details of the JCT Arbitration Rules, see Neil Jones's book *A User's Guide to the JCT Arbitration Rules*.

The option of deleting the arbitration provisions, which caused so much discussion prior to the publication of JCT 80, does not exist in MW 80 but the obligation to comply with the Arbitration Rules is given by the optional deletion of clause 9.5 which also provides for compliance with any amendments to the Rules subsequent to the date of the contract. The parties may jointly request the arbitrator to conduct the hearing in compliance with amended rules. It should finally be added that the parties to any contract can always agree to delete or amend any specific term to a standard form contract.

Chapter 10

GC/Works/2 (Edition 2 1990)

The privatisation in 1989 of the Property Services Agency (PSA), who had previously been responsible for all government funded building work except that for the DHSS, allowed all government departments, with the sole exception of the Royal Palaces but including all national museums and art galleries, to choose their own consultants, type of procurement and form of contract for their projects, and this resulted in the greatly reduced use of GC/Works 1 and 2. It is still however the preferred option of many of them, no doubt because of familiarity with its contents on the past of those in charge of the projects.

Just as government ministries and departments now have their own conditions of contract for major building projects, so they have prepared their own conditions for the smaller project, which in 1990 were defined as those of a value normally of £150,000 or less – the same value as the projects for which MW 80 was designed. It is important to remember that these conditions are for use on central government contracts, all other public sector clients such as the local authorities and statutory undertakers use the JCT Standard and Minor Works Forms. The conditions of GC/Works/2, with Amendments 1–5, therefore, with few exceptions, cover similarly such matters as the intentions of the parties, commencement and completion, control of the works and payment in a similar way to MW 80. Architects engaged on building contracts executed under GC/Works/2 will find little difference in their responsibilities and practice. Since GC/Works/2 is, however, a document produced unilaterally for one particular employer for his own projects, there are certain specific differences and additional provisions, most notably those relating to security passes, photographs and the Official Secrets Act. GC/Works/1 and 2 have in common the endearing habit of referring to building materials as 'things', as for example condition 1(3) which reads: 'in these conditions references to things for incorporation are references to things for incorporation in the Works and references to things not for incorporation are references to things provided for the execution of the Works but not for incorporation therein' which almost justifies the description of 'farrago of obscurities'. This is the exception in a contract which is otherwise drafted in clear and simple English, the sequence of the thirty-seven clauses covering fourteen pages (including the initial clause 1(2) comprising ten definitions) but the clauses appear in an apparently random sequence as they seem to have occurred to the draughtsmen.

For simplicity, therefore, the more logical sequence adopted in MW 80 has been followed in the following commentary and discussion of the major differences. Since GC/Works/2 has both a contents page and a clear side heading to each clause it should not be difficult to find a particular provision.

The recitals and articles

In Government standard forms of contract the recitals and articles are printed separately and not bound in with the conditions as they are in most, if not all other forms, presumably with the intention that the conditions need only then be incorporated by reference. However, as discussed earlier, this can, in practice, lead to problems: for example, the difficulty of finding a relevant condition when it has subsequently been revised, amended or updated, and the difficulty of knowing exactly which set of conditions has been annexed by reference.

Instead of the four recitals and four articles, including the provision for arbitration in MW 80, the GC/Works/2 Abstract of Particulars names the Secretary of State as the 'Authority', the Supervisory Officer (SO) being the architect, engineer or surveyor appointed without any specific person being named. There is provision for a date for completion calculated from the date of an order to commence, the maintenance period for both the works generally and for any other services to be entered. The need for passes if any must be stated. It should also be noted that there is no provision either for quantities or for a quantity surveyor to be additionally named.

The abstract of particulars issued with the other tender documents also includes a standard and a particular specification, drawings and any amendments thereto, any supplementary conditions, such as those referring to liquidated and ascertained damages, a schedule of day work rates, fire precaution requirements, a summary of tender with details of p.c. and provisional sums and proposed 'domestic sub-contractors', all to be completed where necessary and countersigned by tenderers. The form of tender states the tender to be fixed price and includes the anticipated period between the date of acceptance and date for possession.

Definitions

GC/Works/2 follows the convention adopted in Acts of Parliament, statutory instruments, regulations and more recently in JCT 80 of starting with a definition of the particular meaning of certain words. Apart from particularising the 'accepted risks' of fire, explosion, etc., the definitions are in the same general terms as those in JCT 80.

Intentions of the parties

Whereas in MW 68 and 80 the intentions of the parties, including the contractor's obligations, are set out in the first condition in GC/Works/ 2, the detailed provisions requiring compliance with the contract specification and drawings do not occur until condition 8(1)–(4). This also provides for inspection by the SO and for additional tests, other than those in the contract documents, to be at the employer's expense, unless independent tests disclose the work or materials to be faulty, the results of which incidentally are final and conclusive. In this respect GC/Works/ 2 follows JCT 80 more than MW 80, which has no such provision, though neither has the requirement that 'all things' shall be to the architect/SO's satisfaction. The risk that this might relieve the contractor of his obligation to comply with the contract documents is covered in condition 8(4) where the absolute requirement to comply is covered by the statement that 'any things' which do not comply shall be replaced at the contractor's expense.

The duties of the architect/Supervisory Officer

In GC/Works/2 these are not covered in one particular clause as in MW 80, although condition 6 dealing with the SO's instructions gives him wide and fairly undefined powers. In addition he has powers in condition 12 with regard to daywork, condition 13 fire precautions, condition 16 extensions of time, condition 17 sub-letting and condition 24 requiring the contractor 'to complete the works to the satisfaction of the SO' similar to MW 80.

Commencement and completion

These aspects of the conditions are covered in GC/Works/2 in conditions 5, 16 and 19.

Condition 5

Progress of the works differs from MW 80 where the contractor does not have to commence the works on the date for possession but only to complete by the date stated. In GC/Works/2 not only does the contractor have to complete the whole of the works by the date for the completion but he is also given possession of the site or an order to commence 'by notice', in theory without reference to the contractor, although in practice the date for possession is almost invariably fixed by mutual agreement.

Condition 16
This mirrors MW 80 clause 2.4, in that the decision as to when the works have reached completion is entirely at the discretion of the SO and they are to be carried out to his satisfaction. There is no mention in this instance of 'practical completion'. In GC/Works/2 there is an additional requirement that unused materials and rubbish should be removed with the works being delivered up *on or before* the date for completion. There is the same provision as in MW 80 clause 2.2 for the contractor to be granted a reasonable extension for any circumstance 'beyond his control', with the additional requirement for him 'to use his best endeavours to prevent ... and to minimise any such delay ... and to do all that may be reasonably required to proceed with the Works'.

Condition 19
Defects liability is covered in condition 19(1)–(4) and requires, as does MW 80 clause 2.5, that the contractor make good at his own cost and to the satisfaction of the architect any defects which may arise during the defects liability period. There are additional provisions for different sub-contract defects liability periods, which does not exist in MW 80 or JCT 80, and for the express rather than implied right of the employer (referred to in GC/Works/2 as the 'authority') to employ others to make good any contract or sub-contract defects, all consequent costs and expenses to be borne by, and recoverable from the contractor in the event of his default.

Control of the works
This also differs little in substance from MW 80, assignment and sub-letting being covered by GC/Works/2 conditions 15 and 17, SO's instructions, variations and their valuation in conditions 6, 7 and 12, provisional sums in condition 22 and exclusion of persons from the works in condition 33.

Assignment
Assignment under condition 15 is covered in rather more detail than MW 80 clause 3.1. There is no restriction on the 'Authority' from assigning the contract, which could conceivably happen; the contractor is not only

prevented from assigning the contract without written consent, but may not assign any part, share, instalment or other sum of money without consent to the assignment or transfer, such consent to be produced when any payments become due.

Sub-letting

Sub-letting under condition 17 not only requires the consent in writing of the SO (as does MW 80 clause 3.2) but also, under condition 17(2)(a)–(d), requires that the contractor's sub-contract provisions should mirror those of his obligations to the authority, particularly with regard to the ownership of materials, compliance with drawings and specification, site regulations, fair wages, passes and photographs.

SO's instructions

Under condition 6 the SO has only to confirm oral instructions in writing if reasonably so requested by the contractor and then only within fourteen days not two days as MW 80 clause 3.5. In both forms instructions are to be carried out 'forthwith' with the addition in GC/Works/2 clause 6(3) that they shall be 'final and conclusive'.

Admission to the site

Admission to the site under GC/Works/2 condition 33 really covers 'Exclusion' from the site and deals with the matter in a similar way to MW 80 clause 3.4 except that, since GC/Works/2 is used for government contracts, security may be involved. Permission for the employment of aliens is necessary and lists of employees including sub-contractor's employees on the site are to be provided. The contract provides for exclusion of any of them at the absolute discretion of the SO.

Payment

Valuation of variations

The valuation of such instructions as variations is covered in GC/Works/2 condition 7 and, as in MW 80 clause 3.6, are to be 'on the basis of such fair rates and prices as may be agreed'. As in MW 80 clause 3.6, when schedules of rates have been provided with the tender or can be deduced from them, they should be used. The alternative provision in MW 80 for a lump sum to be previously agreed does not exist in GC/Works/2 but in practice it is not excluded where appropriate and sensibly is often adopted.

Dayworks

Dayworks, which are not specifically mentioned in MW 80, are included in GC/Works/2 condition 7(b) for use when valuation based on fair rates and prices cannot be agreed. While these will be used under MW 80 clause 3.6 when the 'relevant prices' are not fair and reasonable, and under JCT 80 when the variation cannot be 'measured', it would appear that under GC/Works/2 condition 7(b) they *must* be used when the authority and contractor cannot 'agree', which would clearly seem to place the contractor in a very favourable position. Under GC/Works/2 condition 12 the contractor is required to produce, for any work 'ordered' to be executed on a daywork basis within one week of the end of each pay week, vouchers with full 'detailed accounts of labour, materials and plant'. There is no requirement for them to be priced and the SO must, if he finds them 'correct', certify one copy and return it to the contractor. On the particular contracts for which these shorter forms are intended this particular obligation, without any amplification of the definition of 'correct', places a difficult, if not impossible obligation on the SO.

Provisional sums

Provisional sums are covered by GC/Works/2 condition 22 in a short clause which does not differ in substance from MW 80 clause 3.7.

Prime cost sums

Condition 21(1)–(4) dealing with prime cost items has, however, no equivalent in MW 80, reference to prime cost sums having been deleted from clause 2 (iii) in MW 68. The provision of $2\frac{1}{2}$ per cent discount (confined to nominated suppliers in JCT 80) covers only the adjustment of the cost in the final account. The 'Authority' has the right to make direct payment but without any restrictions on when it may be appropriate, and there is an obligation on the contractor either to select another in the event of determination of the sub-contract or to execute the work himself.

The contractor is, however, only entitled to such payment as would have been made had the sub-contract not been determined, and while this is to the advantage of the employer it is only likely to be found in unilaterally produced conditions of contract imposed by the larger and most powerful types of client. Otherwise, this clause could well prove to be a suitable alternative to the complexities of JCT 80.

Inconsistencies

Whereas the correction of inconsistencies in the contract documents occurs in the middle of MW 80, at the beginning of the payment section in clause 4.1, the same condition 4(1) in GC/Works/2 appears on the second page. It does, however, set out with much more precision the precedence of the various contract documents. MW 80 only provides in the most general terms for the correction of any inconsistency in or between the contract documents to be treated as a variation and valued as such. In addition, while both MW 80 clause 4.1 and GC/Works/2 condition 4(1) state that the conditions will take precedence over the other contract documents, GC/Works/2 condition 4(2) gives precedence to figured dimensions over those scaled from the drawings.

Progress payments and retention
MW 80 clause 4.2 provides for progress payments at intervals of not less than four weeks in respect of the value of work properly executed and unfixed materials on site, less retention, to be paid within fourteen days of the date of the certificate. GC/Works/2 condition 23 describes these as 'advances on account' and provides for them at intervals of not less than one month. It also includes provision for unfixed materials on site (and credits for old (salvaged?) materials) and the option of proof of payment to sub-contractors, which exists in JCT 80 and MW 80. The question of retention of title, which has caused the JCT so much concern since the *Romalpa* case, is, however, easily resolved by GC/Works/2 in conditions 3(1) and 2(4) which provide *inter alia* for such 'things brought on the site and owned by the contractor, notwithstanding his obligation to protect them against loss, theft or damage, to be included in such advances'.

Payments on and after completion
These are dealt with in GC/Works/2 condition 24(1)–(3) but in a different way from MW 80. The JCT Form provides for payment at practical completion of the contract sum, adjusted for variations and provisional sums less retention and previous payments, to be made within fourteen days.

GC/Works/2 condition 24, however, requires the contractor to be paid the 'estimated final sum' less half the reserve (retention) and, unlike MW 80 which has only a 'penultimate' certificate, 'if he thinks fit', for the SO to pay further sums in reduction of the reserve. The contractor is required under MW 80 clause 4.4 to provide within three months (or such other period as specified) of practical completion 'all documentation reasonably required for the computation' of the final certificate. Under GC/Works/2 he is required to forward a final account to the 'Authority' 'as soon as possible after completion of the execution of the works'. The final certificate of the balance outstanding as defined in condition 1 of GC/Works/2 being issued at the end of the defects liability period once the defects have been made good.

Tax changes

There is no provision in the conditions of GC/Works/2 for recovery by the contractor of changes in statutory contributions, levies and taxes nor in the conditions for the recovery of any increases in the cost of labour or materials during the period for the execution of the works.

Statutory obligations

The contractor is required under GC/Works/2 condition 9 to give all notices required by any Act of Parliament, regulations and/or bylaws of any local authority, public service company or authority, to pay any fees or charges, and to make and supply all drawings and plans as under condition 5.1 of MW 80. On other contracts provision is made for compliance by the contractor with statutory obligations (and notwithstanding anything required in the contract documents to the contrary) the contractor is to be reimbursed for any additional costs arising as a consequence. This does not apply to government contracts, which while having to comply with the principles of the building regulations are technically exempt, and there is therefore, no obligation placed on the contractor to comply.

Value Added Tax

VAT which the contractor may be properly liable to pay in respect of any items executed under the contract, and which is covered in detail in part B of the Supplementary Memorandum to MW 80, is covered in the GC/ Works/2 abstract of particulars and not in the conditions, as are any payments due under the statutory tax deduction scheme.

The prevention of corruption

The prevention of corruption, covered by MW 80 clause 5.5 in local authority contracts, is covered in a similar way in GC/Works/2 32 referring to corrupt gifts and payments of commission.

Should a contract be determined in the event of any corrupt gift or commission having been made, the 'Authority', whose decision is final and conclusive, is entitled to recover the value of it from the contractor. Under MW 80 while the various relevant acts are named and the contract said to be 'cancelled' and not determined, the recovery by the employer includes any loss as a consequence and not just the value of the gift or commission.

Injury, damage and insurance

Government contracts are fundamentally different from those in the JCT forms since traditionally on Government contracts the 'Authority' accepts responsibility for the costs of reinstatement in the even of an accident. The need to define precisely the various responsibilities of the parties to the contract is however exactly the same.

Damage to the works

For this reason GC/Works/2 condition 13(1) and (2) requires the contractor to take all reasonable precautions against the 'accepted' risks defined in clause 1. Those are similar to those in JCT 80 clause 22 and MW 80 clause 6.3A and B, namely fire, lightning, etc., but neither the contractor nor the 'Authority' is required to take out insurance against the financial consequences should one occur.

Similarly condition 14 makes the contractor responsible for damage to his own plant and for making good at his own expense, unless such damage arises from one of the accepted risks or the neglect or default of the 'Authority'.

Injury and loss of property

MW 80 clause 6.1 requires the contractor to be responsible for and to indemnify the employer against all expense, liability, loss claim or proceedings arising in respect of personal injury or death of any person caused by the works (unless it is the fault of the employer). GC/Works/ 2 condition 28 similarly goes to some length to establish the responsibility of the contractor for any injury to persons or damage to any other property contributed to or caused by his neglect. There is, however, no obligation on the contractor to take out any insurance to ensure that he has the necessary finance to meet the obligations for which he is held responsible and consequently no obligation to produce any evidence of such insurance.

Determination

GC/Works/2, being a Government contract, does not of course consider the bankruptcy of the employer as a valid ground for determination by the contractor, as does MW 80 clause 7.2. The other grounds considered in MW 80 – not making progress payments by the due date, obstructing or suspending the carrying out of the works – could arise but are nevertheless not provided for in GC/Works/2.

The 'Authority' is, however, entitled to determine not only the employment of the contractor but the whole contract (condition 26). Whether or not the contract date for completion has passed (elapsed) the contract can be determined if the contractor is guilty of corruption, if he has not complied within seven days with an instruction to rectify defective work, if he delayed or failed to complete the works by the due date, becomes bankrupt, is wound up or if a receiver is appointed – similar grounds in fact to those in the JCT and other forms. A further ground for determination is the contractor's failure to prevent the admission to the site of a person he has been notified by the 'Authority' should be excluded.

Condition 27 of GC/Works/2, like the last part of MW 80 clause 7.1, sets out the consequences of such determination by the 'Authority'. It does not, however, require the contractor to give up possession of the site nor allow the 'Authority' to withhold any further payment until after completion of the works. On the other hand, the contractor is not entitled to any sums outstanding from the 'Authority', who may hire persons previously employed by the contractor, employ other contractors to complete the works, and have assigned to him any sub-contracts the contractor may previously have entered into, to include in the cost of completing the works the cost of making good any defects and cost of supervision.

If the cost of completing the works is less than the contract sum, the balance is to be paid to the contractor. If on the other hand it is more, then the authority may sell *anything* which is on the site, passing on only any surplus proceeds to the contractor.

Additional provisions

Being specifically for Government contracts GC/Works/2 includes, as one would expect, clauses dealing with passes, photography and security. Condition 34 covers the obligation of the contractor to provide to the SO a list of the names and evidence of the identity and bona fides of workpeople on the site to enable him to arrange for the issue of passes. Condition 35 prevents the contractor from allowing photographs to be taken without the consent of the SO and condition 36 draws the contractor's attention to the provisions of the Official Secrets Acts and the 1946 Atomic Energy Act.

There are a further six or seven conditions which do not have an equivalent in the other shorter forms but which could usefully be added.

Condition 2, as has been noted earlier, requires the contractor to satisfy himself concerning, and to allow for all matters which may affect the execution of the works. Clause 10 covers the obligation to provide all necessary protection for the works, security and lighting of the works on site – which is covered in other forms of contract by an appropriate specification clause.

Condition 11 similarly requires the contractor to keep the site free from rubbish and debris arising from the works (but not flytipping thereon). This point of course arises on all contracts and could therefore be included with advantage in other contract forms.

Condition 18 deals with the right of the contractor to object to nominated and domestic sub-contractors and suppliers and with his responsibility for all sub-contractors. Payment to sub-contractors selected by the 'Authority' or by the SO is dealt with subsequently in condition 21.

Condition 25 covers the right of the 'Authority' to deduct from any money due to the contractor any money to which the 'Authority' is entitled under any *other* contract with the 'Authority', which if incorporated in other forms of contract could alleviate local authorities of some of the problems of 'garnishee' proceedings.

Condition 29 incorporates in GC/Works/2 the provision for 'artists and tradesmen' in JCT 63 and 'work by others' in JCT 80 except that in GC/Works/2 the 'Authority' has the power to order such work at any time, whether or not it is described in the contract documents or has the contractor's consent.

Omissions

There is no specific provision in GC/Works/2 for liquidated or ascertained damages, a contractor's representative, fixed price, VAT and statutory tax deductions – although many of these are covered in the abstract of particulars and Property Services Agency standard specification clauses.

Arbitration

MW 80 and other shorter forms provide for the appointment of an arbitrator agreed between the parties or appointed by the President or Vice President of the RIBA or RICS.

GC/Works/2 condition 37(1)–(4) allows for all decisions, other than those which are described as being final and conclusive, to be referred to a single arbitrator to be agreed or appointed by the President of the Law Society (of England or Scotland), the Royal Institute of British

Architects, the Royal Institution of Chartered Surveyors, the Institution of Civil Engineers, the Institution of Mechanical Engineers, the Chartered Institution of Building Services, the Institution of Electrical Engineers or the Institution of Structural Engineers.

While in MW 80 there is no restriction on submissions to arbitration until after practical completion, in GC/Works/2 this cannot take place until after completion, alleged completion, abandonment or determination which if incorporated in other shorter forms would be very much to an employer's advantage.

The clause includes a term that for all cases under English law references are deemed to be covered by the Arbitration Acts, and in Scotland provision is made similarly for a case to be stated to the High Court or House of Lords as appropriate in the event of any question of legal interpretation of the law arising.

Chapter 11

The ACA Form
(Second Edition 1984)

The Association of Consultant Architects (ACA) issued their Form of Building Agreement in 1982 as an alternative to the alleged over-complexity of JCT 80. The advent of the JCT Intermediate Form two years later, with ostensibly the same objective, is considered by some to have eliminated the need for the ACA Form, notwithstanding its many innovatory provisions. At the same time a *Guide* to the form (Form and Guide published by the Architectural Press) stated the ACA's objectives in drafting the contract – 'to provide an "alternative" form which could be used with or without quantities, with all or only part of the drawings provided by the architect, with the option of either five grounds or none to justify an extension to the contract period, and with the choice of adjudication, arbitration or litigation'.

The form runs to twenty-five clauses over ten pages, and although starting with the ostensible object of being simple and easy to understand, it needed a twenty-two page guide paraphrasing the original in layman's language, to make the provisions 'easier to assimilate'. Although each clause and sub-clause is clearly annotated with side headings, they are set out in the same random sequence as JCT 63 and 80 but are considered here for ease of comparison in the same sequence as MW 80. The wording of many of the clauses establishes entirely new principles and new responsibilities from those previously considered, and each clause should therefore be studied extremely carefully, line by line, to ensure that both parties clearly understand their obligations at the outset. This is particularly important in view of the absence to date of any supporting case law when this form has been used.

A second edition of the ACA Form was published at the end of 1984 at the same time as a British Property Federation edition. The 1984 ACA edition incorporates 12 major revisions and a number of minor amendments effecting a considerable improvement over the earlier edition and resulting in a much more acceptable document.

The recital and articles

These differ little from those of the JCT forms with provision for the use of the term supervising officer (SO) if someone other than an architect is nominated. A major difference, however, was the obligation on the contractor to execute, complete and 'maintain' the works for the duration of the 'maintenance' period (see also clause 12). While this may have been an appropriate phrase in civil engineering works, where the 'maintenance' of a dam or a bridge was unlikely to be unduly onerous, it would seem to suggest problems in, for example, an office block where it could be held to include cleaning windows and even the daily maintenance of floors (perhaps even waste paper bins?).

In the 1984 edition the words 'and maintain' were deleted, leaving only the obligation of the contractor to 'execute and complete' the works.

There is also provision for the inclusion of the option of bills of quantity, reference to a 'Time Schedule' in the appendix, in which are inserted the dates for possession, completion (taking over), the rate per week of liquidated and ascertained damages, and the length of the defects liability (maintenance) period.

A new seventh recital (G) in the 1984 edition defines a working day as being Monday to Friday, excluding bank holidays and those under the Building and Civil Engineering Annual Holiday with Pay Scheme.

The contractor's general obligation

The contractor's obligations are covered in clauses 1.1 to 1.7 where, in addition to executing and completing the works in clause 1.1 the contractor has to comply with instructions 'issued' by the architect (1984 revision) with no longer any reference to whether they were mentioned in the agreement or not.

In clause 1.2 the contractor has to 'exercise all the skill care and diligence to be expected of a properly qualified and competent contractor experienced in carrying out work of a similar scope, nature and size' – a phase which could well be incorporated into JCT contracts.

Clause 3.1 in the 1984 edition makes the contractor responsible for all mistakes, inaccuracies, discrepancies and omissions in his own drawings, details, documents and information, the existence of which (i.e. contractor's drawings) is ignored in the JCT contracts.

The 1984 edition also added the requirement that the contractor's designated Works should comply with any performance specification and should be fit for the purpose for which they were required – in effect a warranty similar to that provided by NSC2 for JCT 80, and the RIBA/CASEC Agreement for use with the JCT Intermediate Form IFC 84.

Clause 3.2 obliges the contractor to submit the drawings etc. in accordance with the 'Time Schedule' which could also with advantage be incorporated in the JCT Forms.

The architect's duties

The architect's duty to provide the contractor with two copies of drawings or details as are reasonably necessary to amplify the contract drawings is given in clause 2.1 in a similar way to that in the JCT forms, the contractor to give the architect notice of when he requires them 'proximate' to the date when they are necessary.

It is important to note that clauses 2.1 and 2.2 are repeated with the alternative text, the second being for use when the contractor is responsible for supplying the balance of the detail drawings. Additional clauses are provided in this instance, clauses 2.3 and 2.4 requiring the architect to 'comment' (thereby correctly escaping the responsibility that would have followed had he 'approved' them) within fourteen days and not to depart from the contract or statutory requirements.

The 1984 edition substituted the word 'artificial' for 'physical' obstructions, the discovery of which the contractor had to notify to the architect, who in turn had to confirm the contractor's proposals for dealing with them in a similar way to that of an engineer under condition 12(1) of the ICE Form.

Clause 3.3 obliges both contractor and employer to maintain confidentiality of the contract documents and their prices, although the employer may use them for the purposes of 'execution, completion, manufacture, repair, advertisement, letting or sale of the works'.

Clause 4.3 of section 4 'Visits of the Work by the Architect' covering the architect's visits to the site, has now been deleted.

The employer's liabilities

The employer's liabilities are covered by clauses 7.1 to 7.4, where, as in the JCT forms, the cost of any 'damage loss or expense' to the contractor arising from disturbance of the regular progress of the works is to be reimbursed, subject in clause 7.2 to the contractor giving notice 'upon it becoming reasonably apparent', with an estimate and supporting evidence required within twenty-eight days. If the contractor fails to comply with this, he is debarred from recovery before the final certificate in clause 7.3. This is an odd provision since it presumably allows the contractor to claim at this late stage which negates the earlier requirement. Clause 7.4 allows the whole matter to be 'adjudicated' if adjudication is chosen. The quantity surveyor's role is defined in clause 14 (instead of in the articles and recitals) where he is named and assigned the duties of 'negotiating' with sub-contractors and providing certificates under clauses 9.6, 15 and 16. This differs from MW 80 where the quantity surveyor has no specific role.

Commencement and completion

Clauses 11 and 12, dealing with commencement and completion, run to three pages and thirteen sub-clauses with four further optional clauses.

The obligation of the employer to give possession on the date stated and the contractor to proceed regularly and diligently are detailed in clause 11.1 and the architect is required to certify if the works are not completed in time in clause 11.2.

Extension of contract period

This is provided in one or other optional clauses 11.5. In alternative (1) the architect cannot grant an extension except for any act, instruction, default or omission of the employer or the architect. In alternative (2) four other events are added, *force majeure*, 'an insurable risk', war or delay by a local authority or statutory undertaker. In either case the contractor must give notice immediately the event becomes reasonably apparent, with supporting particulars, and the architect must then under clause 11.6 grant an extension within eighty-four (calendar?) days. This procedure is the same as under the JCT forms except that there the architect grants only such extension as is reasonable. An opportunity to review extensions, similar to that in JCT 80, is covered by clause 11.7.

In clause 11.9 the contractor is required to revise the time schedule to take account of any adjustment to the contract period the architect may have made and to submit it within fourteen days to the architect for his consent.

Damages for non-completion

These are provided for in one or other optional clauses 11.3. In the one *the architect* deducts from any certificate due the appropriate liquidated and ascertained damages, in the other *the employer* is 'entitled to recover from the Contractor such damage, loss and or expense'. In the opinion of the present author this second option, with damages at large to be argued over, is clearly not in the employer's interest, but this view is obviously not shared by the authors of the form.

Acceleration or postponement

Clause 11.8A, which has no equivalent in any JCT form, empowers the architect to instruct the work to be brought forward or postponed and allows for the contract sum to be adjusted accordingly.

Practical completion

This is termed 'taking over' in the ACA Form and is covered by detailed procedures in clause 12.1. It differs from those in the JCT forms in requiring the contractor to notify the architect when he has finished (accompanied by a list of things he has not yet done but promises to do, and which the architect can either accept or replace with his own list!). The date on which the works are actually considered complete and ready for take-over during this exchange of lists is far from clear.

Defects liability

Defects liability is covered by clauses 12.2 and 12.3. In the former, the contractor must, if so instructed at any time during or within fourteen days of the expiration, carry out 'all necessary repairs, replacements and remedial work' (by implication including those for which the employer might otherwise be responsible). Under clause 12.3 this is to be at the contractor's expense unless in the opinion of the architect it is due to the employer's use, occupation, negligence, omission or default, which it would seem could lead to endless arguments.

Partial occupation

Partial occupation (clause 13) is permitted with the consent of the contractor, with provision for a proportional abatement of liquidated and ascertained damages as in the JCT forms.

Control of the works

Assignment and sub-letting (sub-contracting)

These are covered in no less than nine sub-clauses. Clause 9.1 precludes either party from assigning without the written consent of the other in the usual way, but with a particular proviso specifically permitting the contractor to assign any monies due to him (which is not considered necessary in any of the other shorter forms). In clause 9.2 the architect's prior consent to sub-letting is required, without the need for him to be 'reasonable'.

The contractor's representative

This is covered in a separate clause 5. Under 5.2 the contractor is required to provide a site agent, previously approved by the architect, as a full-time representative not to be replaced without the prior written consent of the architect. This raises the interesting question of whether the architect will have previous knowledge of or will interview the proposed agent, and of the consequences of the contractor subsequently proposing to dismiss or transfer him as a result of the architect withholding or delaying his consent. There is an additional obligation in clause 5.3 for employees of the contractor to be skilled, qualified and experienced in their respective trades. One wonders if the reference to 'callings' implies that those who have taken holy orders will be employed on the works also! The clause enabling the architect to exclude unsuitable employees from the works appears in 8.1.

The management of the works
This is laid down under clause 5.1 as a separate and overriding obligation to 'provide all necessary inspection, superintendence, supervision, planning and management of the Works ... to ensure the proper performance of the Contractor's obligations'. This also does not occur in other forms and one wonders if it might not have been better included as part of the contractor's general obligations in clause 1.

Sub-contractors
Sub-contractors are then covered in detail in the following seven sub-clauses. Firstly, sub-clause 9.3 allows the architect to name a single sub-contractor or supplier in the contract documents. Secondly, if instead of naming an individual, a list of names is given, the architect can either select one person or instruct the contractor to do so and then submit the name to him for approval, subject always to the contractor's right to object to the name selected by the architect.

Architect's instructions
These may be issued for any one of fourteen reasons (and by implication no other) under clause 8 at any time up to the final certificate but the contractor does not have to comply with them for fourteen days until he has informed the architect under clause 17 of the cost and effect on completion. The first seven reasons cover as usual work not in accordance with the contract, dismissal from the works, testing, alterations to access, limitations of working space and working hours, alterations of the design, quality or quantity of the works, and matters relating to the execution, completion and maintenance of the works under clause 8.1(g). (The reversion to alphabetic sub-clauses is presumably an error in draughting

and the generality of sub-clause 8.1(g) would seem to render the preceding six and the following seven superfluous.)

Oral instructions are to be confirmed in writing within seven days under clause 8.3. As in MW 80 clause 3.5, under ACA Form clause 12.4 should the contractor not comply with the architect's instructions the employer may, subject to having given the contractor seven days' notice, employ others to do the work and deduct the cost from the contract sum.

The architect's authority to issue instructions at any time up to practical completion ('Taking-Over of the Works') in the 1984 edition is qualified by the proviso 'save as otherwise provided in clause 8.1 and 12.2 (Defective Outstanding Work)'.

The valuation of architect's instructions

Clause 17.1 requires the contractor to estimate the value of instructions (the opposite of JCT). Under 17.2 the period in which the architect has to agree the contractor's estimates was changed in 1984 from seven days to five working days, after which the contractor must proceed as instructed.

The valuation of instructions, other than those arising from the negligence of the contractor, is required under clause 8.2 to be carried out in accordance with clause 17. This provides for the contractor, and not the quantity surveyor, to inform the architect within fourteen days of the estimated cost and effect on completion of any instruction or correction of a discrepancy in the contract documents. The procedure is then laid down in clause 17.2. If these are not agreed within five working days (or such other period as is inserted) then either: (i) the contractor is instructed to proceed; (ii) the instruction is cancelled; or (iii) the matter is referred to an adjudicator. In the present author's view, whether included in the contract conditions or not, this is unlikely to be achieved in practice. Clause 17.5 allows the architect *before* or *after* issuing an instruction to dispense with these provisions and fix the cost based on the schedule of rates, and/or grant a 'fair and reasonable' extension. This seems to follow the 'heads I win, tails you lose' principle and is unlikely to prove acceptable to contractors.

Should the contractor not avail himself of the opportunity within the fourteen days to estimate the cost or extension under clause 17.1 he is then debarred from so doing prior to the final certificate. Whether he can then do so at that time is unclear.

Assignment and sub-letting (including naming)

Provisional sums are referred to in clauses 9.4 and 9.5, cross referenced to the payment clause 16.6 and adjusted under clause 9.6 for those sub-

contractors and suppliers named and described in the contract documents. Where the work is not so described and therefore included in the
contractor's tender, but a provisional sum is included for instructions to
be issued after the contract has been let, the contractor is required under
clause 9.6 'to negotiate and agree a price' on 'compatible' conditions. The
architect is to be invited to all meetings and discussions in connection with
these negotiations and is to receive copies of all documents, correspon-
dence and sub-contracts: a very necessary provision but one which is
likely to deter architects from delaying the selection of sub-contractors
until after the contract is let, just as the complexities of NSC 1, 2, 3 and
4 deter them from nominating sub-contractors under JCT 80.

Should a contractor, for reasons not of his own making, be unable to
enter into a sub-contract he 'shall select another person to an equivalent
standard and quality' – which would seem to permit the employment of
just such a sub-contractor as the nominating procedure was designed to
prevent. There is no provision for any employer/sub-contractor agreement, notification and direct payments in the event of default by the main
contractor, which may or may not be a good thing.

Clause 9.7 requires the contractor, in the event of determination of the
sub-contract, to find and instruct another at his own cost which, in view
of the unforseeable nature of this eventuality, would seem to present
problems to contractors in knowing how much they should allow in their
tender to meet this obligation.

Clause 9.8 contains the surprising obligation on the main contractor to
be fully responsible to the employer for the design of, and compliance
with any 'performance' specification for the sub-contract work which,
although attractive in its simplicity, seems hardly likely to be acceptable
to a building contractor.

Clause 9.9 also ensures that the contractor remains fully resonsible for
the due performance and is in no way relieved of his responsibility for all
works, whether sub-contracted or not.

Employer's licencees

Clause 10 provides for artists, tradesmen and statutory undertakers, if
included in the contract, to be engaged by the employer, and (as in JCT
80) for the contractor to be reimbursed for any resultant direct loss and
expense.

Payment

The contract sum

The contract sum is to be adjusted for any one of twelve reasons under clause 15. These arise primarily from variations, direct loss and expense or delayed completion.

Correction of errors and inconsistencies

These are covered similarly to MW 80. In ACA clauses 1.4 and 1.5 the architect is required to determine and certify a fair and reasonable adjustment to the contract sum to take account of the correction of any mistake, omission or 'mis-description' in the contract bills (no mention of SMM here). In clause 1.5 the contractor is not only to exercise skill, care and diligence in the execution of the works but must also 'ensure there are no ambiguities or discrepancy in any of the Contract Documents' – a task which no doubt is made easy or difficult depending on his knowledge of the skill, care and diligence of the architect.

Progress payments

Under clause 16 progress payments are to be based on an interim application, with supporting documentation, presented by the contractor (not the quantity surveyor) on the last working day of each calendar month, following which the architect has fourteen days in which to issue an interim certificate. The guidance notes suggest that an alternative date can be made by agreement, since offices with more than one contract would otherwise be unduly busy in the middle of each month. Alterations to printed conditions are always to be deprecated and one would have thought this clause introduced unnecessary complications, it being preferable to have retained the accepted provisions in other contracts for certificates on a 'monthly' basis.

This certificate, which is to include all work up to the date of the contractor's valuation, specifically excludes by clause 16.2(a) work which, in the opinion of the architect, has not been properly executed as well as unfixed materials (not incorporated into the works), which at a stroke, although perhaps not without some extra cost to the employer, attempts to remove the problems arising from *Romalpa* and *Dawber Williamson* type situations. Also excluded are adjustments previously agreed or certified, and all amounts previously certified. Under clause 16.3 the certificate is to be honoured within fourteen days of the date of the certificate (presumably the date of issue not date of receipt).

Retention

Retention is covered in clauses 16.3 to 16.5. It is important to note that retention is not deducted from the value of work executed before certification by the architect, but by the employer paying 95 per cent of the amount certified. It is hoped that employers will understand this subtlety and not write out their cheque for the full amount of the certificate. Under clause 16.4 the employer has no option but to place the remaining 5 per cent in a separate bank account and to act as a trustee – which differs from MW 80 clause 4.2 where the retention monies do not have to be so invested. Under ACA clause 6.4, however, the contractor is not entitled to the interest and clause 16.5 includes the useful provision for the employer to deduct from this fund any money due to him from the contractor. Clause 16.6 provides for the adjustment of the contract sum in respect of the value of any sub-contracts or supplies executed and for which a provisional sum was included.

The final certificate

There is no release of half the retention at the time of the employer 'taking over' the works, and the final certificate (which in any case is not final by virtue of clause 19.3) specifically excludes the contractor from relief of any future liability which may arise subsequent to the issue of the final certificate. This should really have been printed in red capital letters. As the guidance note states, 'no certificate relieves the contractor of any liability', and the lawyers will no doubt have much to say in the years to come about the effect of these words. The final certificate is therefore only a certificate releasing the balance of monies due to the contractor and is to be issued only when the contractor has completed all his obligations, twelve weeks after the end of the 'maintenance' period or twelve weeks after receipt of the contractor's final account, whichever is the later. As with other certificates of money this certificate has also to be honoured within fourteen days of its issue.

Fluctuations

If clause 18 is deleted the contract is truly on a fixed price basis, with no provision for recovery by the contractor even of any unforeseen increases in statutory contributions, levies or tax changes, such as occupy twenty-six sub-clauses in small print in part A of the Supplementary Memorandum of MW 80. If the clause is retained, however, then (in three commendably short sub-clauses) the conditions provide for the contractor to be paid 80 per cent of any increase or decrease in the cost of work certified in interim certificates up to the contract date for 'take-over', based on an ACA single index for the month prior to the date of the contractor's application. This index is based on the 59 individual monthly provisional indices published for the Board of Trade by HMSO. The final contract sum is to be similarly adjusted in the same proportion.

Statutory obligations

Statutory requirements

As in the JCT forms, if it becomes apparent to the contractor that the contract documents, drawings, details or instructions issued by the architect will result in statutory infringement, he is required to inform the architect, who is required to issue instructions under clause 1.6 for its resolution. Any instructions issued as a consequence may entitle the contractor to payment valued as a variation under clause 8.2.

The contractor is required under clause 1.7 to make all the usual applications, give notices and pay all fees to comply with the statutory requirements (unless the architect instructs him to the contrary). In this case, presumably, the architect or employer will do so themselves, since in the event of a breach it is the contractor who is liable, and to say that he had been told not to by the architect would be no defence in law – only a mitigating circumstance. The contractor is to indemnify the employer against all damage loss and/or expense in respect of any breach which would appear to conflict with the previous clause, which states that he may be paid for complying with an instruction to put it right. The cost of all fees paid by the contractor are to be added to the contract sum unless they are provided for in the contract documents, in which case the contract sum is to be adjusted accordingly. In the past these fees mostly applied to the fees of district surveyors in the Inner London area but since 1980 they are now incurred for all local authority building inspections.

Value Added Tax

VAT is covered as clause 16.7 by three lines, rather than in the fifteen sub-clauses in part B of the MW 80 Supplementary Memorandum. The ACA Form simply and effectively places the obligation on the employer to pay the contractor the total amount of any VAT which may be properly charged by the contractor and makes no attempt to particularise.

Statutory tax deductions

These are dealt with rather more extensively in the optional clauses 24.1 to 24.4 although still in considerably less detail than in MW 80.

Why it was considered necessary in this case and not when dealing with VAT is not clear, unless it was thought that while most employers were familiar with the former, they were less likely to understand the latter, particularly if they were unknowingly employing a 'contractor' within the meaning of the Act and were thereby liable for the additional payment of any tax for which they were properly liable; not having made the necessary deductions from any payments due to an uncertified main contractor ('sub-contractor'!).

Fair wages resolution and prevention of corruption

The ACA Form does not include such clauses. The former having been repealed, there is clearly no case for inclusion of a fair wages clause. Should the Form be used for a local authority project no doubt the JCT MW clause on the prevention of corruption could be incorporated.

Antiquities

Two additional clauses were added to the ACA Form in 1984. Clause 14.1 provides for all fossils, antiquities, structures, remains and other objects of geological or archaeological interest to be the property of the employer and 14.2 requires the contractor to leave them undisturbed and undamaged and to notify the architect, who then issues the necessary instructions which are valued accordingly. This is clearly an essential requirement in view of the provisions of the current legislation for the protection of sites of archaeological importance.

Injury, damage and insurance

As discussed in an earlier chapter, the insurance clauses in JCT 80 and MW 80 were of necessity detailed and complex. Notwithstanding ACA clause 6.1, which transfers ownership of goods and materials to the employer only when incorporated into the works, responsibility for loss and damage, whether incorporated or not, remains with the contractor until the works are taken over by the employer.

Injury to, or death of persons

This is covered in the usual way in clause 6.3(a). The contractor must be liable for, and is to indemnify the employer against, any claim respect of injury to, or death of any person arising out of the works on or off site, with the proviso that the contractor's liability shall be reduced proportionately by the extent of any contribution arising out of the negligence, omission or default of the architect, employer, servants or agents. This differs from the usual phrase 'unless due to any act or neglect of the employer', which no doubt reflects the current practice of the courts in apportioning blame.

Damage to property

This is covered in a similar way in clause 6.3(b). The contractor is required in both cases to take out and maintain, together with any sub-contractors' insurance, cover for not less than the sums stated in the contract documents. In view of the possibility of no such amount being stated in the other contract documents, there is the additional requirement, as in MW 80 clauses 6.1 and 6.2, for the contractor to maintain 'such insurances as are necessary', and provision for the employer to approve the 'terms and conditions' of the contractor's insurances, which in the absence of specific amounts might often be advisable.

Insurance of the Works

In the case of new work this is dealt with by the contractor insuring in joint names, and by the employer insuring for work to existing buildings. It follows the established precedent except that in the case of new work the risks are unspecified, being 'all those contingencies against which the contractor can readily obtain insurance', and the contractor is required to enter his policy number.

Subsidence and collapse

The equivalent of clause 19(2)(a) of JCT 63, which is not in MW 80, is provided by ACA clause 6.5, covering damage to adjoining property *except* that arising from negligence of the contractor or from errors or omissions in the designing (not design?) of the works (as this would appear to have been included in clause 6.3). Also excluded are damage which can reasonably be foreseen to be inevitable (and one can foresee the profits accruing to lawyers in that!), work to existing buildings which has been insured by the employer and uninsurable risks arising from nuclear perils or war. The employer has, under clause 6.6, the usual opportunity to approve the firms, terms and conditions (if he is competent) of the contractor's insurances, and the contractor, under clause 6.7, is to pay all premiums promptly and produce evidence accordingly, both of his own and of those of his sub-contractors. Should he not do so, under clause 6.8, the employer may pay these himself and deduct the cost from the contract sum. Under clause 6.9 he may likewise make a claim at the contractor's expense, should the latter fail to do so.

Determination

The grounds in the ACA Form for determination, either by the employer or the contractor, are inevitably broadly similar to those in MW 80 and the other shorter forms, both on the grounds of equity and in order to stand up in the courts.

Determination of the employment of the contractor by the employer
This is provided for in clause 20.1. (The word 'Termination' being used
instead of the more usual 'determination' is presumably of no consequence.) However, in addition to the two grounds in MW 80 of lack of
diligence or suspension of the works by the contractor, and financial
failure, three further grounds are added in the ACA Form: assignment or
sub-letting by the contractor without consent, refusal to comply with an
instruction and any other breach of the agreement. Many would feel that
the drastic step of determination was a fairly harsh measure for such
breaches. However, the contractor has fourteen days to remedy the
breach, which he does not have in MW 80. If provisions for adjudication
are included in the contract then the matter can be referred to the
adjudicator within this period.

Termination of the contract by the contractor
In this case, under clause 20.3, termination is on the usual grounds of non-
payment, interference with certification, obstruction of the work for more
than four weeks or the employer's insolvency, and the contractor must
give fourteen days' notice, not seven as in similar provisions for
adjudication.

Termination beyond the control of the parties
There is a new provision under clause 20.4 which allows either party to
terminate after three months if delay arises from *force majeure*, damage
by an insured risk, war, riot or 'disorder'.

The consequence of termination
These are set out in clause 22, and in the case of the employer
'terminating', are spelt out in more detail than in MW 80, with a
certificate from the architect on completion of the works certifying the
balance due from either party to the other. If the contractor terminates,
he must 'protect and secure the Works'. When termination is for reasons
beyond the control of the parties, no payment for any consequential
damage, loss or expense to either side is allowed. The contractor must
return the site to the employer and also any drawings, details and
documents he himself has prepared, the copyright becoming automatically vested in the employer.

Disputes
These provisions are probably the most radical in the contract. The
parallel of the increasing complexity of standard forms of contract and

the demand for their simplification follows closely that of the increasing length of the process introduced by the 1979 Arbitration Act and the need for a simpler and quicker method of resolving disputes either through the High Court or by arbitration.

MW 80 provides for any dispute to be referred to an arbitrator agreed between the parties or appointed by the President or Vice President of the RIBA or RICS and unless the shorter two options of the three JCT Rules are chosen, it may well take several years before pleadings and further and better particulars are exchanged, and the dispute between the parties is finally resolved. It is regrettable that in order to ensure that neither party is put at a disadvantage, arbitration procedures have now become so formalised that there is little difference between the procedure for bringing a dispute to arbitration and that of taking a case before an Official Referee or the High Court. The legal costs, only some of which are recoverable, apart from the addition of the arbitrator's fees and the hire of the rooms for the duration of the arbitration, are identical. The proceedings are equally drawn out, for the date of the hearing is dependent on the availability not only of counsel, leading and/or junior, but also of the judiciary or arbitrator. As with a court hearing, this can frequently result in the date being set for an arbitration twelve months ahead.

The ACA Form of Contract provides three options for the settlement of disputes between the contractor and the employer, or architect on his behalf:

(1) adjudication
(2) arbitration
(3) litigation

Adjudication
Adjudication has previously only been used in the resolution of disputes between contractor and sub-contractor. ACA clause 25 provides for an adjudicator to be named and 25.2 provides for certain matters to be referred to him. These relate to: (1) adjustment or alterations to the contract sum, i.e. the valuation of variations or direct loss and expense; (2) extensions of the contract period (time for taking over the works); (3) compliance of the works with the contract documents; (4) entitlement to determine. Since extensions of the contract period arise because of delays in completion and not delays in progress, disputes on this subject are unlikely to be resolved by adjudiction prior to practical completion. They

are usually of such a complex nature that they are unlikely to be satisfactorily resolved in such a short time.

The adjudicator is required to give his decision within seven days of the dispute being referred to him and he is to be paid within thirty days thereafter (in direct contrast to arbitration where, in view of the natural reluctance of parties to pay for decisions not in their favour, the decision is sensibly not given until the arbitrator has been paid). The decision of the adjudicator is not however final and binding since, although the contractor must comply with the decision and proceed diligently until the works are taken over, the matter can still then be referred to arbitration by either party. In practice the diligence of the contractor, in the event of an unfavourable decision, is likely to be more nominal than real. If the arbitrator fails to give his decision within seven days or refuses to act, another can be appointed by the Chairman at the time of the ACA. The decision of this second adjudicator is, however, final and binding on the parties unless objection is made within twenty-eight days. Should any decisions of the adjudicator be referred to arbitration however, any other related disputes, including those with sub-contractors or suppliers, can be referred (joined) to the arbitrator if they have not already been referred to another.

The arbitrator has the usual powers to review *inter alia* any decision, certificate or valuation of the architect or the adjudicator, and if the arbitrator is not the adjudicator, as he may be under clause 25.6 (i.e. both judge and jury on his previous decision!), he may be called as witness. The argument that this will concentrate the adjudicator's mind in reaching his earlier decision would seem to be of doubtful validity as is the ability for parties to 'agree to the contrary'!

There is, finally, provision for the conditions to be governed either by English or Scots law, with the proviso in the latter case that while the Arbitration (Scotland) Act of 1984 will apply, section 3 of the Administration of Justice (Scotland) Act of 1972 will not, if the parties do not wish to be allowed the option to 'state the case' to the High Court for the interpretation of a point of law.

It is the present author's view that, just as too easy grounds for determination are not a good thing, neither is this easy provision for challenging decisions of the architect ultimately in the best interests of either party and, since the adjudicator's decisions can subsequently be referred to arbitration, it is of little value.

In 1984 a new line was added to the adjudicator clause 25.1 permitting the adjudicator to delegate his duties to another who must give his decision within five working days of having been requested to do so.

Clause 25.3 requires the contractor to proceed with the works diligently, whether referred to adjudication or not.

Arbitration
The provisions for arbitration are again more detailed than those in MW 80 and cover a similar, but not identical list of decisions of the architect which may be challenged:

- the construction of the agreement
- adjustment or alterations of the contract sum
- extensions of the contract period
- the compliance of the works with the contract documents

and in addition
- 'any other matter of whatsoever nature' including anything left to the discretion of the architect.

These disputes are to be settled by the architect within seven days and his decision must be complied with. This would seem to restore the architect to the position of quasi-arbitrator, despite the fact that this reverses the decision in *Sutcliffe* v. *Thackrah* (1974) and contradicts the statement in clause 25.2 that the architect in giving this decision is acting as an expert and not as an arbitrator. However, under clause 25.3 the decision may be referred to an arbitrator after takeover under the same conditions and sub-clauses as those included for adjudication.

Litigation
The third option, which will satisfy the view of certain solicitors specialising in building disputes that judges are better than arbitrators in resolving disputes, excludes both adjudication and arbitration, providing only for disputes to be considered by the courts under English or Scots law, as appropriate, (building contracts in Scotland may be executed under English law if so stated in the contract documents).

Additional provisions
Additional provisions in the clause 3.1 of ACA Form include an important reference to precedence of one contract document over the other – that is, as in MW 80 clause 4.1, unless stated otherwise, the contract conditions take precedence.

ACA clause 4.1 requires the contractor to give the architect and his (not the employer's) representatives full access to the works, workshops and other places where work or goods are being prepared or manufactured in order to test, inspect or examine them. Clause 4.2 appears to repeat in similar terms the option for the architect to do so if he wishes.

Clause 23.1 requires communications between the architect, contractor and employer to be in writing, and to be delivered or sent by first class post, which is deemed to have been received two days after posting. Clause 23.2 confirms singular to include the plural and vice versa, persons to include firms and corporations, headings and marginal notes (missing in the case of clause 15) to be inserted for convenience only.

Chapter 12

Other shorter forms IFC84, JCLI, SBCC, ASI and NEC

Whereas architects have little option but to use MW 80 for the smaller local authority projects and GC/Wks/2 for central government projects, for certain private sector projects there is also the Intermediate Form (IFC84), the Joint Council for Landscape Industries (JCLI) Form for Landscape Works, the Scottish Building Contracts Committee (SBCC) Form for Minor Building Works in Scotland, the Architects & Surveyors Institute Minor and Small Works Forms, the New Engineering Contract (NEC) and the JCT Conditions of Contract for Building Works of a Jobbing Character.

The Intermediate Form IFC 84

The contract conditions of the JCT 80 edition for use without quantities were published at the same time as the with quantities version and were identical, with merely the reference to bills of quantities omitted from the clauses referring to contract documents, the valuation of variations and interim certificates. In all other respects the contract clauses were identical.

It was therefore immediately apparent to those using the without quantities form, and to the RICS in particular, that the form as drafted, with the complex and intricate procedures for nominations for instance, was totally inappropriate for their needs.

How could it be otherwise when the scope of the work was of necessity so different? There was therefore a yawning gap between the simple clauses of the minor works shorter forms and the full JCT with quantities edition for contracts for new work in excess of a quarter of a million pounds.

In this the RICS were supported by the architects, 90 per cent of whose contracts were of a value of £250,000 or less but who nevertheless needed to be able to select specialist sub-contractors with some protection for the employer against design defects by the sub-contractor, who in turn demanded some protection against the financial failure of the main contractor.

Notwithstanding the patent advantages of the shorter forms, it is obvious that on contracts of a larger value the architect's opinion of what is fair and reasonable (for example in the valuation of variations) may not coincide with that of the contractor, and some more detailed rules are required if the contractor is not to consider the relatively high costs of litigation outweighed by the need to reduce or eliminate a serious financial loss.

Under these circumstances the shorter forms are clearly inadequate and consideration had therefore to be given to the use of JCT 80 either with or without quantities. In the past the only difference between these two forms had been the reference to inclusion of bills of quantities in the contract documents, and their use for the valuation of variations and interim certificates.

This, however, is no longer the case, since the publication of the JCT Intermediate Form 1984 which attempted to bridge the gap for those projects where the conditions of MW 80 were not sufficiently explicit and where the detailed provisions of JCT 80, particularly those dealing with nominated sub-contractors and retention, were too cumbersome and complicated for the amount of money involved.

Its existence over the past nine years has proved the conditions of the Intermediate Form achieve the right balance. Since they allow for the alternative inclusion of bills of quantities it has made deep inroads into the sales of JCT 80, as has MW 80, which now sells over seven times as many copies as JCT 80 with quantities.

Positive guidance on the use of the JCT Intermediate Form IFC 84 is set out on the back cover of the form which states that it is suitable when the building works are:

(1) 'of a simple content involving the normally recognised basic trades and skills of the industry.
(2) without any building service installation of a complex nature or other specialist work of a similar nature.
(3) adequately specified or specified and billed as appropriate prior to the invitation of tenders.'

The Practice Note IN/1 goes on to elaborate that, although the form

'has been prepared, so as to be suitable for contracts, for which the more detailed provisions of the Standard Form 1980 editions are considered by the Employer or by his professional consultants to be unnecessary in the light of the foregoing criteria [the form] would normally be the most suitable form for use ... where the contract period is not more than 12 months and the value of the works is not more than £250,000 (1984 prices) but this must be read together with paragraph 14 on the money limits within which the use of the Minor Works Form (MW 80) may be appropriate.'

The Practice Note then continues:

'The Intermediate Form may however be suitable for somewhat larger or longer contracts, provided the three criteria referred to in the endorsement are met, but Employers and their Professional consultants should bear in mind that the provisions of the Intermediate Forms are less detailed than in the Standard Form 1980 edition and that circumstances may arise, if it is used for unsuitable works, which could prejudice the equitable treatment of the parties.'

The informed reader will however have already noted two inconsistences in these statements:

(1) If there are to be no building services installation of a complex nature involved, why then should the RIBA and CASEC combine to produce an Employer/Sub-contractor Design Warranty specially for use with this Form?

(2) If the form is 'suitable for contracts for which the contract period is not more than 12 months' why has the Tribunal included in the form the option of a clause for the contractor to recover increased costs by the formula method – accepted throughout the industry as being applicable only for contracts of over one or two years' duration?

A third less widely known, but equally relevant point is that up to the last moment before publication the upper limit in the Practice Note was £500,000 not £250,000 and it was only on account of the need to publish the Form without further delay that the RIBA, in response to continued pressure from Building Employers Confederation, agreed to the substitution of the lower figure of £250,000.

It is clear that, since there were no last-minute changes in the content of the Form itself, there is no doubt as to the suitability of the Form for some contracts at the higher figure.

Choosing the appropriate form depends on a careful evaluation of all aspects of the project and is clearly a matter on which the client should rely heavily on the expertise and experience of his architect.

IFC 84 is structured in exactly the same way as MW 80. After the recitals and articles, the contract conditions are grouped under the same headings of Intentions, Possession and Completion, Control of the Works, Statutory Obligations, Insurance and Determination. This similarity to MW 80 may lead one to think that the wording is the same; it is similar but certainly not the same, with several major differences and additions such as, for example, those dealing with named single sub-contractors, extending the contract period and determination. There are also additional clauses, such as those dealing with deferring the date for possession, granting extensions after the completion date, remedial work and testing work similar to that already found defective.

The RIBA was insistent on the inclusion of detailed grounds justifying an extension to the contract period, provisions for naming a single sub-contractor, rules for the valuation of variations and provision for bills of quantities (not found in MW 80), and also stated that it was desirable for provisions to be made for partial possession, levels and setting out, access for the architect and clerk of works, work not forming part of the contract (artists and tradesmen), and the recovery by the contractor of direct loss and expense if the employer or his architect delayed the regular progress of the work.

Compared with the seven pages of conditions in MW 80 and the 46 pages in JCT 80 with quantities, the 17 pages of IFC 84 seem to strike the right balance between the brevity of the Minor Works Agreement and the detailed complexities of the Standard Form. It has all that the RIBA and RICS initially asked for, with the additional advantages of clauses dealing with deferred possession, defective work and reference to the High Court.

The major differences in the conditions of IFC 84 compared with MW 80 are set out below.

Article 5.3 provides for the parties to go to the High Court on disputed points of law (which they always could do anyway).

1.   Intentions of the parties

1.2   Quality and quantity of work
IFC 84 alone of all the JCT forms sets out the priority of the contract documents i.e. the quality and quantity of the work shall be that set out in the contract bills; if there are no bills it should be that set out in the specification or schedules; and if there are neither bills nor schedules, in

the event of any inconsistency between drawings and specification, that shown on the drawings shall prevail.

1.4 Instructions as to inconsistences
The architect shall correct any inconsistency in the contract drawings, levels, quantities, named sub-contract tender or departure from SMM, and by implication the contractor must also exercise reasonable skill and care in notifying the architect of any.

1.5 Contract bills
Departures from the Standard Method of Measurement must be expressly stated.

1.10 Unfixed materials on site
Unfixed materials may not be removed from site without the consent of the architect and any that have been included in a certificate become the property of the employer, notwithstanding the obligation of the contractor to remain responsible for any loss or damage to them.

1.11 Unfixed materials off site
Similarly unfixed materials off site become the property of the employer; the contractor is responsible for any loss, damage, storage and insurance, whether their value is included in a certificate or not.

2. Possession and completion
(not commencement and completion as MW 80)

2.2 Deferment of possession
If so stated in the Appendix, the employer may defer the date for possession for a period which should (shall?) not exceed six weeks, although the contractor is then entitled to 'direct loss and expense'.

2.3 Extension of time
Although similar to MW 80, clause 2.3 provides explicitly for the architect to extend the contract period *after* the completion date and up to 12 weeks after practical completion (as JCT 80). This is notwithstanding the contractor's obligations to use his *best* endeavours to prevent delay to the reasonable satisfaction of the architect and to provide such information as is necessary for the architect to come to a decision.

2.4   The (relevant) events

These generally follow JCT 80 (as distinct from MW 80 which refers to 'reasons beyond the control of the contractor') and include delay in completion arising from testing satisfactory work, and the two optional clauses for shortages of labour or materials which the contractor could not have foreseen at the date of tender (10 days earlier). It does not allow for delays caused by named sub-contractors.

2.6   Certificate of non-completion

The architect must certify as in JCT 80 (but not required by MW 80). He must then cancel if superseded by a subsequent extension and clause 2.8 requires any liquidated damages which may have been deducted to be repaid.

2.11   Partial possession

This does not appear in the conditions but is set out as an option in the JCT Practice Note IN/1 for incorporation if required.

3.   Control of the works

3.3   Named persons as sub-contractors

Work described for pricing by the contractor to be executed by a named person shall be executed by the contractor under the Standard Form of Sub-contract on the basis of the Standard Form of Tender NAM/T. If the contractor is unable to do so on account of any particular condition, the architect has to either issue an instruction changing the condition, omit the work or substitute a provisional sum.

However, if the work is covered by a provisional sum, the named sub-contractor must still tender on the standard form NAM/T and on receipt of this the contractor has 14 days in which to object once the identity and details of the named sub-contractor are known.

Quite rightly the consequences of the unsatisfactory performance of the sub-contractor and any subsequent determination are also covered, but in a different way to JCT 80. The contractor must keep the architect informed of any events likely to give rise to a determination e.g. lack of diligence. In the event of determination before completion, the architect must name another sub-contractor (when the contractor gets an extension but no loss and expense), instruct the contractor to carry out the work himself or omit the work altogether, in which case the contractor becomes entitled to both an extension *and* loss and expense.

Clause 3.3.7 confirms that, whether or not the sub-contractor is responsible to the employer for any design of the sub-contract works, the main contractor is not responsible for anything other than the goods and workmanship required.

3.5   Architect's instructions

These must always be in writing. There is no provision in IFC 84, as exists in MW 80 and JCT 80, for oral instructions which have to be subsequently confirmed in writing.

3.7   Valuation of variations

Whereas under MW 80, the valuation of variations must be by the architect on a fair and reasonable basis, using relevant prices in the priced specification or schedules, IFC 84 requires variations to be valued by the quantity surveyor in accordance with the prices in the contract documents. If the work is similar in character and executed under similar conditions and quantities, the rates must be similar to those in the contract documents. If the work is not similar it must be a fair valuation; and if dayworks are appropriate these are to be in accordance with the RICS/BEC definition. All valuations must include preliminaries but not 'direct loss and expense'.

3.8   Provisional sums

The architect is to issue instructions as to their expenditure.

3.9   Levels and setting out

These are to be provided by the architect by accurately dimensioned drawings as in JCT 80.

3.10   Clerk of works

The employer's right to appoint a clerk of works whose 'duties shall be to act solely as an inspector' is provided as in JCT 80 but without any arrangements for him to issue 'Directions'.

3.11   Work not forming part of the contract

This follows the JCT 80 artists and tradesmen clause where the contract documents so provide.

3.12   Instruction as to inspection – tests

As in JCT 80.

3.13   *Instructions following failure of work*

An entirely new clause requires the contractor to notify the architect of his intentions with regard to any work similar to that which has been found to be defective and to make good at no cost to the employer. If the architect is not satisfied, he can instruct further opening up at no extra cost, and if the contractor objects the matter can be referred to arbitration.

3.14 *Removal of work*

As in JCT 80, the architect has the power to order the removal of defective work (but without the authority to accept remedial work).

3.45   *Postponement*

Power is given to the architect to postpone any of the work.

4.   Payment

4.1   *Contract sum*

Any errors or omissions, other than those between the contract documents corrected under clause 1.4, are deemed to have been accepted, and not to affect the contract sum (stick or bust).

4.4   *Interest on percentage withheld*

When the employer is not a local authority retention is held in trust for the contractor 'without the obligation to invest'.

4.5   *Computation of the adjusted contract sum*

The contractor must send to the architect, or if so instructed the quantity surveyor, all documents required for the final valuation 'within a reasonable time'.

4.6   *Issue of final certificate*

To be honoured within 21 days, not 14 days as in MW 80.

4.7   *Effect of final certificate*

Conclusive evidence that those items the architect has reserved to be to his 'reasonable satisfaction' are satisfactory.

4.8   *Other certificates*

Not conclusive evidence.

4.9 Fluctuations
Either:
   (a)   fixed except for tax fluctuations, or
   (b)   formula with provision for 'freezing' increased costs after the contract completion date.

There is no provisions for recovery of increased costs by single index or the 'traditional' method.

4.10 Fluctuations – named persons
Similar provision for named persons.

4.11 and 4.12 Disturbance of progress
Similar provisions to JCT 80 and preserving the contractor's common law rights.

5. Statutory obligations
The clauses are similar to MW 80.

6. Injury, damage, insurance
The clauses are similar to JCT 80.

7. Determination
The provisions on determination are similar to JCT 80 except the contractor has no entitlement to recover loss or expense when his employment is determined through *force majeure*, loss or damage to the works by the insured risks or civil commotion. Clause 7.8 brings together those grounds for determination which are neither the fault of the contractor nor the employer.

8. Interpretation
Articles are to be read as a whole; the date of tender is 10 days before date for submission; schedules are to be priced; and 'person' means an individual partnership or body corporate.

Footnote
For a more detailed explanation of the JCT Intermediate Form see *A Commentary on the JCT Intermediate Form of Building Contract* by Neil F. Jones and David Bergman – BSP Professional Books, 2nd Edition, 1990.

JCLI Form of Agreement for Landscape Works

The Joint Council for Landscape Industries first published the Form of Agreement for Landscape Works in April 1978 when, with certain additional provisions appropriate for landscape work, it was otherwise almost identical in context and format to the then current MW 68. This had been agreed with the JCT in order to reduce the proliferation of forms covering similar work and to ensure its widespread acceptance by local authorities. However, since the designation of 'landscape architect' is not protected as is the use of the name 'architect' by the Architects Registration Acts, there was no need for the alternative 'Supervisory Officer' to be added to the words 'Landscape Architect'.

The April 1982 edition similarly mirrored MW 80 while still incorporating the additional clauses incorporated in the 1978 edition and the relevant clauses have kept in step with subsequent amendments to MW 80 since that date.

Partial possession (clause 2.6)

While partial possession of the works is considered unlikely to arise on minor building works, the same is not true of landscape work where, perhaps, the need to delay planting from one season to the next might occur. Provision is therefore included for an additional clause 2.6 which, although it was not envisaged when the contract was entered into, allows the employer, with the consent of the contractor, to take possession of part of the works and allows part of the retention to be released accordingly in a similar way to that in JCT 80.

Plant failures (clause 2.7)

As in the JCT forms, the landscape contractor is responsible for making good any defects, including plant failures, which may arise from any cause other than vandalism prior to practical completion. (Vandalism is dealt with separately in clause 6.5).

After practical completion, however, the situation is somewhat different. Whereas the employer can clean the floors and windows of a building during the defects liability period without the risk of causing any damage to the works, the same is not true of living items such as grass, trees and shrubs, where injudicious or inadequate maintenance can result in their early demise. The JCLI Form therefore provides, in clause 2.7, for one of two options for the soft landscape (planting) part of the works.

Clause 2.7A covers the event where the contractor is responsible for the upkeep of the works during the ensuing defects liability period. In this case any grass, shrubs, ordinary stock trees and semi-mature or advanced nursery stock trees found to be defective at the expiry of the respective periods specified are to be replaced by the contractor entirely at his own cost.

Under clause 2.7B if the employer chooses to be responsible for upkeep after practical completion, he and not the contractor is responsible for any plant material which is subsequently found to be defective.

Objections to a nomination (clause 3.8)

Since clause 3.7 still refers to the prime cost sums which were omitted from in the Minor Works Form after 1980 it follows that the implied reference to nomination should be covered by the contractor's corresponding right of objection. This is provided in clause 3.8 where the contractor can make reasonable objection to the nomination of a particular sub-contractor or to one who is insisting on sub-contract conditions which conflict with those of the main contract.

Retention (clause 4.3)

Should a substantial proportion of the plants (i.e. over 10 per cent) not have survived until the date of practical completion, a provision in clause 4.3 allows for the value of these plants to be deducted at practical completion prior to the release of the first half of the retention monies.

Fluctuations (clause 4.6B)

It was considered that the period for the execution of works under MW 80 was unlikely to exceed twelve months and therefore, as with GC/Works/2, the contract should be on a fixed price basis without provision for the contractor to recover any unforseen increases in the cost of labour and materials after the date for the submission of tender. Since, however, it was possible that work under the JCLI Form could extend, either initially or as a result of extensions to the contract period, over two planting seasons, recovery for increased costs was clearly essential.

Fortunately, there is a separate category 49 for landscape works in the Board of Trade monthly indices of increased costs of labour and materials. Should it be considered appropriate for either the main landscape contract or any sub-contract, any variation in price of the works subsequent to the date of tender can be simply calculated and the contract sum and progress payments adjusted accordingly.

Malicious damage and theft (clause 6.5A)

It cannot be denied that the risk of damage from vandalism and theft prior to practical completion of the works is greater for landscape work than for general building. The JCLI contract therefore provides two alternatives, the first like MW 80, for all theft or malicious damage prior to practical completion being made good at the contractor's expense, who is therefore obliged to include in his tender such amounts as he deems appropriate to cover the consequences of such damage as may arise.

Clause 6.5B
Alternatively a provisional sum to cover the cost of making good such damage can be included instead under clause 6.5B, when the employer undertakes to reimburse the contractor out of the provisional sum provided for making good such damage on a nett cost basis, paying the contractor no more and no less than the replacements have actually cost.

Scottish Building Contracts Committee Form for Minor Building Works
Of the various shorter forms of building contract discussed in this chapter that of the Scottish Building Contracts Committee (SBCC) is unique in that it is the only one whose sponsoring organisation is directly represented as a full constituent member of the JCT, with the consequence that while no changes to any of the JCT forms can be made without its approval, the SBCC produces its own form independently, incorporating its particular requirements without reference to the JCT.

The SBCC not only produced a supplement to the JCT 80 for use with the Standard Form in Scotland, but it also produced its own Form for Minor Building Works. This form is clearly modelled on MW 68 but takes account of Scots law and practice. For example the form starts with a statement of the considerations, with the offer and its acceptance, and ends with the signatures of the parties.

SBCC Minor Works clause 3 specifically requires the contractor to comply with Acts of Parliament instead of any 'statute, any statutory instrument, rule or order or any regulation or bylaw applicable to the works'. In clause 8 reference to existing structures is omitted and the period of insurance is limited until practical completion so that the contractor is responsible for insuring the works and the employer the existing structures and contents. An optional clause B is then added for the employer to insure both the works and the existing structures and contents. Clause 10(ii) regarding the penultimate certificate has been reworded as clauses 12(ii) and 13(iii) covering the rights of determination in the event of financial failure. As one might also expect, the appointment of an arbiter (or arbitrator) in the absence of agreement is to be by a sheriff and not by the President of the Chartered Institute of Arbitrators, and his remuneration is also dealt with. There was, however, no provision for the implementation of the Finance (No. 2) Act 1975 – the statutory tax deduction scheme – and this has been covered by an addendum included in later reprints.

Being similar to MW 68 in so many respects there was no provision for naming a quantity surveyor, schedules, valuing variations in accordance with contract prices or adjustments to the contract sum on account of changes to levies and taxes, as were incorporated in MW 80.

It is not surprising therefore that the Scots felt the need for a revision to their Minor Works Form and in 1981 a revised draft was prepared by the Royal Institute of Architects in Scotland, restructuring the clause into a more logical sequence as MW 80 had done, but grouping them under the three headings of 'Duties of the Contractor', 'Duties of the Employer' and 'Miscellaneous Provisions'.

Use of the Minor Works Form 80 in Scotland

There is no reason, however, why MW 80 should not be used, unamended, by the insertion of a line in Recital 1 to read 'and subject to the proper law of this contract being English law'. The parties to any contract can choose the law which shall be applicable to their contract and the courts will enforce this. For example, it is not uncommon for civil engineering work being carried out in the Middle East to be made expressly subject to English law. The use of a contract in an English form may however raise the implication that the proper law of the contract is to be English law. So it is better to avoid such ambiguity by the insertion of an express term as to what is to govern the contract.

Three things should be distinguished:

(1) 'The proper law' of the contract: namely by what law the parties have agreed, expressly or by implication, to have their contractual obligations determined.
(2) 'The law of the place where the contract is to be performed' which would determine the law to be applicable under clause 5.1, for example, where the contractor undertakes to comply with all statutory obligations including building regulations.
(3) 'The law of the place where any arbitration takes place', the *lex fori*. The present wording of Article 4 is perfectly appropriate if the parties intend to hold any arbitration in Scotland. In general, the law of the place where an arbitration takes place determines the procedure but it should be remembered that Scots procedure is entirely different from English: see John Parris: *Arbitration* (1983).

It appears to be undetermined whether the parties can provide for an arbitration to take place in Scotland subject to English procedure but it is certain that, in the absence of express agreement, any arbitration in Scotland will be subject to Scots law even though the proper law of the contract is English law.

The Architects and Surveyors Institute (ASI)

Formerly two organisations, the Faculty of Architects and Surveyors and the Construction Surveyors Institute amalgamated in 1989. This has resulted in the three previous FAS lump sum contracts, the 1980 Minor Works, 1981 Small Works and the 1986 Main Contract, now being titled ASI Forms, although the text remains unchanged.

The November 1978 revision to the June 1975 edition of the FAS Form of Building Contract was fully revised, updated and rewritten as the March 1986 edition. This increased the previous edition of 14 pages to 31, with provision for use with and without quantities and with clauses in a section headed format 'primarily intended for larger or complex jobs'. Also provided were FAS Sub-contract and Contract of Sale Forms for nominated sub-contracts and suppliers. With appropriate attestation clauses for use under seal it is suggested that the Form would be suitable for local authority contracts also. In its enlarged form it is clearly no longer a 'shorter' form and is therefore outside the scope of this book.

ASI Small Works Contract (December 1981 Edition)

The 13-page ASI Small Works Contract December 1981 edition is not to be confused with the 8 page ASI Minor Works Contract (October 1980) (described on pages 152–155). The Small Works Contract is described as being 'intended for use with smaller works (such as private houses, or alterations, or extensions) described by drawings and for a specification or schedule of works, but not using a bill of quantities. It provides for nominated sub-contractors and suppliers, and also for fluctuations if required. It should not be used for more complex works or be regarded as a substitute for the ASI Building Contract. The Form may be used for local authority contracts provided the appropriate attestation part is used to complete the contract under seal.'

In October 1983 a single page supplement was published, listing 13 revisions to the recitals and conditions to permit the form to be used with bills of quantities and for a quantity surveyor to act.

No figures are available for the numbers of the various forms of contract sold by ASI but it is understood to be favoured by building surveyors and the smaller architectural practice. The new ASI 1981 Small

Works Contract also follows the section headed format of the JCT MW 80.

The recitals and articles

The ASI Small Works Contract provides in the recitals for its use with a specification/schedule of works/drawings, prepared by a named architect/surveyor/engineer, acting on behalf of the employer and thereinafter referred to as 'the Architect', with the proviso that the description 'Architect' in the recitals must be deleted unless the professional acting is registered under the Architects Registration Acts. If he is not so registered, then the description architect is deemed to be changed to 'Surveyor/Engineer' accordingly. Otherwise the recitals and articles differ little from these in the JCT forms except that reference to the provision of prices by the contractor has been transferred to clause 1.4 and, like MW 80, arbitration to its former traditional position at the end of the form under 'Disputes and Arbitration' in section 10. The arbitrator, as would be expected, is to be appointed under the Arbitration Acts by the then President of the Architects and Surveyors Institute.

The intentions of the parties and contractor's obligations

These are set out in sections 2 and 1. The architect's role and instructions are clearly set out in 10 clauses and sub-clauses in section 2. His obligations to represent the employer, inspect the work in progress, certify payment and to administer the contract are set out in 2.11 and to act without partiality to either party in 2.12. His powers to inspect work in progress and to reject sub-standard work is spelt out clearly in 2.2 which also states that he is not responsible for any failure by the contractor to carry out and complete the work to 'the terms' of the contract. Oral instructions are to be confirmed by the contractor within seven days and complied with, in the absence of any dissent, within a further seven days. In the event of non-compliance within 14 days of an instruction, the architect may instruct others under clause 2.31 and deduct the extra cost from money due to the contractor. The possibility of the contractor requiring further detail drawings and/or instructions from the Architect is envisaged in clause 2.4, the contractor having to give 'fair and reasonable notice to the Architect having regard to the time factor' – a slightly ambiguous phrase?

The contractor's obligations and documents are covered by 15 clauses and quite properly occupy the first page of the conditions. They include the obligation to carry out (but not complete?) the work in accordance with the contract documents (clause 1.1), properly and efficiently to a standard of finish to the architect's satisfaction (clause 1.2) (hopefully without relieving the contractor of his liability under clause 1.1). The contractor is required to notify the architect of any differences in the drawings and specification (differing from what – presumably each other?) who then decides which is to be followed. The contractor is responsible not only for setting out the work from dimensioned drawings supplied by the architect and rectifying at his own expense any errors, but must also 'observe and conform with the provisions of the Health and Safety at Work etc. Act/Regulations'.

Commencement and completion

Section 4 under the heading 'progress, defects' starts with the obligation of the contractor to proceed diligently and expeditiously and to be responsible for any delays except (as in MW 80) for those 'beyond his control'. Commencement, completion dates and damages for non-completion are to be inserted in the spaces provided in clause 4.1. The contractor is required to do his best to progress the work and must promptly notify the architect when delay becomes apparent. The architect in turn grants an appropriate extension under 4.4 if warranted.

In the event of non-completion by the contract date, the contractor pays the employer the liquidated damages for the period of delay certified by the architect.

Practical completion when 'approved' by the architect is defined in clause 4.2 as being 'when the works are finished fit and ready for handover to and use by the Employer with only acceptable minor items to be completed' (but without the more helpful provision of fitness for use).

Defects due to defective materials, workmanship, including frost and adverse weather conditions (presumably only prior to practical completion) are listed by the architect under clause 4.3 at the end of the defects liability period (six months) and are to be made good properly and promptly by the contractor. The clause specifically does not exempt the contractor from liability for any subsequent latent defects, a phrase which could have also been usefully defined. Clause 4.6, for some reason, is not used and clause 4.7 deals at some length with the procedures for notices by registered post four weeks after the general call up of men on the outbreak of 'hostilities' (ignoring the fact that one may precede the other). War damage is to be repaired or protected as instructed by the architect.

Control of works

Section 3 under the heading 'Workmanship, plant' and section 5

'Subletting, sub-contracts' deal with the work on site. Section 5 prohibits the assignment of the contract and requires the contractor to list for the architect items he intends to sublet with details of firms, any one of which the architect may reject, but in which case the contractor may declare a substitute. What happens then is not clear. The employer may also determine the employment of the contractor if excessive subletting or non-declaration is involved. This clause should really have gone into section 9.0. As in other forms, the contractor is still responsible for the adequacy and quality of the work (notwithstanding clause 1.2).

Nominated sub-contractors, and suppliers, whose work is covered by a prime cost sum, may be selected by the architect and engaged on similar sub-contract terms to those of the main contract, the work to be started and co-ordinated by the main contractor, who remains responsible for their performance, and who has the right of objection to their appointment under clauses 5.3 and 5.4. Clause 5.6 permits the appointment of artists and tradesmen engaged by the employer where these are previously specified and with the reasonable consent of the contractor if not.

Materials, workmanship and plant are covered in 13 clauses, section 3 starting with the statement that they shall be 'the best of their respective kinds' (thought by some to be too subjective a requirement), in accordance with the contract documents. The requirement to comply with the relevant Agrément Board Certificates which certify appropriateness rather than quality is strange, but the requirement to conform 'at least' to the latest British Standards and Codes of Practice, with vouchers to establish compliance, is a useful one not found elsewhere.

The need for a competent foreman in charge on site at all times, empowered to take instructions, and the employment of adequately skilled workers, who can be excluded from the site, is covered in clause 3.2. Protection of the works from the weather, watching and lighting are covered in 3.3, sample tests and opening up at the employer's expense (unless this establishes non-compliance) in 3.4 and 3.6, with work necessary following an emergency covered in 3.7.

Variations are dealt with in detail, instructed by the architect when extra work, changes or omissions are required and valued not on 'a fair and reasonable basis' but by the architect at the prices in the prices specification or schedule of rates, at rates or by a quotation or on a daywork basis approved by the architect before the work proceeds. What happens if the architect does not approve the dayworks is not stated.

Interim, final certificates and payments

These are covered by two pages of clauses and sub-clauses in section 6 under the heading 'Financial matters'. Interim payments are to be made only on architect's certificates at monthly intervals, based on details provided by the contractor, 'checked' by the architect and valued by the quantity surveyor, if the employer has engaged one. They are issued within 14 days of the contractor having applied for one and honoured by the employer within 14 days of the architect having certified it. Certificates should include the gross amount due, including that due to nominated sub-contractors and suppliers, and unfixed materials not prematurely brought to site, which then becomes the property of the employer, less retention and amounts previously paid (not previously certified so architects must ensure previous certificates are paid in full).

The amount of retention is to be inserted in the space provided, figures of 5–10% dependent on the size of the contract being suggested. The final account is to be submitted by the contractor at or soon after practical completion (how soon?).

Value Added Tax is to be added to the contract sum and recovered from the employer in accordance with the relevant acts, rules and regulations of Customs and Excise.

Nominated sub-contractors and suppliers are also dealt with in an unusual amount of detail for a minor works contract. Provisional sums are properly defined as being gross including overheads and profit for 'builder's' work in clause 6.71, and nett inclusive only of $2\frac{1}{2}\%$ or 5% 'cash' discount on the trade price for nominated sub-contractors and suppliers respectively against which prime cost sums have been included in the contract documents under clause 6.72. Interim payments to nominated sub-contractors and suppliers under clause 6.8 are certified by the architect and notified to the sub-contractor, who may be paid direct if payment is not received from the main contractor within 17 days. Similar provisions under 6.82 apply to nominated suppliers who are to be paid in full less only 5% cash discount within 30 days of the end of the month in which delivery is made.

The final certificate is issued by the architect under clause 6.9 after all sub-contractors' receipts have been submitted to him and all defects made good. *No* certificate is conclusive evidence that the work has been executed in accordance with the contract documents.

Fluctuations in statutory charges are allowable under clause 7.3 and in labour and materials (if not deleted) under clause 7.4 on the basis of 'quantified' claim statements and evidence submitted by the contractor for approval.

Discrepancies

The contractor must notify the architect under clause 1.54 of any differences he finds in (not necessarily between?) the drawings and specification, and the architect must decide which is to be followed. These are not, however, described as variations and the contract makes no reference to the recovery of any extra costs which may be incurred by the contractor.

Statutory obligations

The contractor is obliged to comply with all legal and statutory requirements and must notify the architect before making any changes to conform with these; he is entitled to a variation order if warranted. All fees and charges are set against a provisional sum or added to the contract. The contractor is to pay any VAT due under clause 6.6. There is no mention of the Finance No. 2 Act of 1975 nor of the prevention of corruption.

Insurance

Insurance against damage to the Works is dealt with either by the contractor insuring in joint names for new work (clause 8.1) or at the sole risk of and insured by the employer (clause 8.2) in the case of work to existing buildings. Either party is entitled to insure himself and deduct the cost of the premiums from monies due in the event of default by the other. The usual insured risks against damage to the Works are defined in clause 8.61 and the nuclear exclusions in 8.62.

Clause 8.4 requires the contractor to give the employer an indemnity and requires the contractor to insure against all liability for injury or death of persons and damage to property other than the works (irrespective of any negligence by the employer or the contractor).

Determination

Determination by the employer in clause 9.1 follows MW 80 with the additional ground for determination if the contractor refuses to comply within 14 days of a written notice the instructions of the architect, and the usual right to employ another contractor to complete the works, delaying any further payment to the determined contractor until the work has been completed by the second contractor. The recovery of any direct loss and expense incurred by the employer arising from the determination from the contractor is specifically covered in 9.17. Determination by the contractor is only possible if the employer fails to honour a certificate within seven clear (?) days of a written notice by the contractor pointing out that the period for payment has expired, if the employer delays the work for four weeks or more or becomes bankrupt. The contractor is entitled to the reimbursement of any direct loss and/or expense which he has incurred as a result of the determination.

Claims

The ASI Small Works Contract differs from MW 80 in that a further clause has been included at the end of the determination section. Clause 9.4, under the sub-heading 'Claims', requires the contractor and/or a nominated sub-contractor to submit any claim for direct loss and/or expense in writing not later than four weeks from the date of practical completion, citing relevant clause numbers, reasons and financial details.

The absence of any specific events, such as exists in JCT 80 clause 26 under which (and only under which) a contractor is entitled to the recovery of any direct loss and/or expense, in the ASI Small Works Contract is a serious deficiency and may well mitigate against its widespread use.

The ASI Minor Works Contract (October 1980 Edition)

This was published in October 1980, and perhaps by no coincidence, nine months after MW 80. The Faculty of Architects and Surveyors, who had not previously published a contract for minor works, issued one differing from their standard form by adopting a similar grouping and sequence of clauses to MW 80. It was, however, unique in several ways. Firstly it adopted the word 'Advisor' instead of 'Architect/Supervising Officer', presumably to enable it to be used by building and quantity surveyors. This also had the questionable advantage of enabling the form to be used by anyone, however qualified (or, indeed, unqualified).

In common with MW 80, the ASI Minor Works contract covers four pages and is divided into similar main clauses and sub-clauses. The difference is that there are separate sections called 'Workmanship, Plant, Sub-letting, Variations/Fluctuations'. Commencement and completion clauses are headed 'Progress, Defects'. Payment is headed 'Financial Matters'.

The contract starts with three recitals and four articles with the provision for arbitration covered in clause 10, with the appointment of an arbitrator by the President of the Architects and Surveyors Institute, the choice being final and binding on both parties. No provision is made for pricing the schedules by the contractor, for the valuation of variations, nor for the naming of a quantity surveyor as occurs in MW 80.

Intentions of the parties

The intentions of the parties are covered in clauses 1 and 2. The obligation on the contractor to proceed with due diligence and expeditiously is not specified until clause 4.1, but earlier in clause 1.2, he is made responsible for the proper and efficient execution of the works and is also allowed to suggest variations to assist the efficiency of the work to a standard of finish to the 'advisor's' satisfaction. Clause 3.1 repeats the well-worn specification phrase that materials and workmanship should be 'the best of their respective kinds in accordance with the qualities and details described'. (Should they not be so described the contractor presumably has no obligation to provide them?)

The architect/SO's duties, or as this contract terms them 'The Advisor's Role', are covered in clause 2 where, in addition to preparing the design and particulars of the work (contract document) as in MW 80, the 'advisor' is required to issue further (not any) information and instructions as necessary, these to be confirmed in writing. In addition, the advisor *will* inspect the work in progress on behalf of the employer and has the power to reject work not in accordance with the contract document. As in the JCT forms, however, the advisor under clause 2.2 is not responsible for any failure by the contractor to carry out and complete the works 'to the terms of the contract'.

Commencement and completion

These are covered by clauses 4.1, 4.2 and 4.3. The contractor is relieved of responsibility if completion is delayed for reasons 'beyond his control'. For these the 'advisor' shall grant an extension 'if the circumstances warrant it'. The amount of liquidated and ascertained damages are included in the same clause. Practical completion and the defects liability period are covered in clause 4.2 with the addition in note 1 of the definition that practical completion means 'when the works are finished fit and ready for hand-over to and use by the Employer with only acceptable minor items to be completed'.

In clause 4.3 the responsibility of the contractor to make good defects is set out in similar terms to MW 80 with the additional specific responsibility for 'latent' defects.

Control of the works

The form has no specific clause under this heading, such responsibilities being included in clauses 1, 3, 5 and 7. Clause 1.4 restricts any extras to those authorised in writing by the 'advisor'. As in MW 80, clause 3.1 allows him to exclude employees of the contractor from the works and clause 3.2 requires the contractor to keep on the works a person in charge to 'discuss the work' and take instructions as if 'deemed to have been issued' to the contractor.

Clause 5.1, like MW 80 clauses 3.1 and 3.2, precludes the contractor from assigning or subletting any part of the contract without written consent and clause 7 not only permits the 'advisor' to issue variations but stipulates (not on a fair and reasonable basis in accordance with the contract rates as MW 80 clause 3.6) that they shall be valued, if the contract rates are not appropriate, on the basis of rates agreed before the commencement of the work by a quotation or on a daywork basis.

Payment to the contractor (financial matters)
These are dealt with in clauses 6 and 7.3, with the option of either a single payment on completion of the work, the making good of defects and the presentation of the contractor's account, or interim payments made from time to time *at the discretion of the 'advisor'*. Receipts for materials or goods to prove ownership are required and payment is to be made within fourteen days of receipt of the certificate by the employer under clause 6.3. Retention in accordance with the percentage to be inserted is to be held *in trust pending proper completion and the issue of the final certificate* under clause 6.4. The contract conditions are silent on the question of increased costs of labour and materials except that clause 7.3 states that changes in statutory payments imposed on the contractor shall be set against the contract sum, the meaning of which is regrettably obscure.

Statutory obligations
The contractor is required under clause 1.3 (three lines instead of the six in MW 80) to comply with all legal and statutory requirements and to pay all fees and charges. Under clause 5.2 he is required to comply with the requirements of the statutory tax deduction scheme as required by the Finance No. 2 Act 1975 covered in part C of the MW 80 Supplementary Memorandum. Value Added Tax is covered in clause 6.6 which provides for it to be recovered in a similar way in accordance with the 'relevant' acts, rules and regulations. The contract is silent on the question of corruption covered by the MW 80 optional clause 5.5.

Insurance
Insurance against damage to the Works is covered in clauses 8.1 and 8.2, the contractor to insure in the joint names in the case of new work, and the employer to insure for work to existing buildings, with the option for the other, to insure and deduct the cost in the absence of proof.

Reinstatement is to be put in hand forthwith on acceptance of the claim under clause 8.3. Any injury to any person or damage to any property, including subsidence, collapse and the ingress of water, arising out of or caused by the works, is also the responsibility of the contractor under clause 8.4 and he is required to maintain the necessary insurance.

Determination

Determination by the employer in the event of lack of diligence or suspension of carrying out the works (clause 9.1) is almost identical to MW 80 clause 7.1, with the additional provision in the event of non-compliance with an 'advisor's' instruction, the employment of another contractor but without any reference to delaying payment until completion. Determination by the contractor (clause 9.2) also follows MW 80 clause 7.2, except that there is no provision in the event of the employer suspending, as distinct from delaying, the works.

The New Engineering Contract

Whereas the Institution of Civil Engineers Standard Form of Contract, the ICE Conditions, is a remeasurement contract suitable for very large civil engineering projects and therefore does not come within the scope of this book, their New Engineering Contract (NEC) published in 1993 is stated to be suitable for all types of engineering and construction contracts large and small, and therefore deserves inclusion.

Like the ACA Form it is designed to cover all types of remeasurement contracts including with contractor's design, prime cost and management. All versions are, however, designed for collaborative management with a project manager of undefined discipline taking a leading part.

All types of contract consist of a standard printed Form of Tender, a Schedule of Contract Data (part of which is to be completed by the employer and part by the tenderer) a set of core clauses set out under nine headings similar to MW 80 applicable to all types of contract, six sets of main option clauses dependent on the type of procurement selected, a set of secondary option clauses under a further 13 headings, some of which are appropriate to only certain of the main options, covering provisions such as fluctuations, liquidated damages, sectional completion, early completion bonus, contractors' design liabilities etc. The 95 core clauses occupy 18 pages with a further single-page addendum of six main option clauses for a standard lump sum contract without quantities, so that it comes at the top end of the shorter forms.

In spite of its non-traditional approach, requiring a radical reappraisal of contract responsibilities, information required from the various parties to the contract, and the precise intention of unfamiliar terms and phrases, it is written using plain words in relatively short clauses so achieving clarity and aiding comprehension.

Time alone will tell if in practice it achieves the comendable objectives claimed for it.

Building Works of a Jobbing Character JCT JA/C90
Like the ASI Minor Works Contract, the JA/C90 conditions of contract are intended for small works where the MW 80 provisions are thought to be too detailed. It is primarily intended for employers who have buildings requiring continual repairs and minor alterations for which instructions are issued either by their own works orders or by use of a standard form of tender and agreement JA/T90 with an annexe describing the works and identifying any drawings or specifications; details of the commencement and completion dates, and insurance being included on the form of tender. It is envisaged that the form will be suitable for work to a value of no more than £10,000 (at 1990 prices) with a duration of less than one month with a single payment on completion.

The conditions of contract are published separately and incorporated in the works order or agreement by reference and comprise only 20 short clauses set out under the usual nine section headings covering only four pages.

(1) *Intention of the parties*
 The printed conditions to prevail (1.1); the contractor to proceed with due diligence (1.2); the employer to provide any further information necessary.

(2) *Commencement and completion*
 The dates for commencement and completion to be as the tender or works order; the employer to give a fair and reasonable extension for reasons beyond the contractor's control (2.1); the defects liability period to be six weeks (2.2).

(3) *Control of the works*
 The employer's written instructions will be complied with forthwith (3.1); valuations are subject to objection by the contractor (3.2); valuations by agreement, by the employer and may include direct loss and expense (3.2).

(4) *Payment*
 The contract sum is VAT exclusive. The contractor to submit an invoice inclusive of variations on completion (4.1); the employer

to agree within 28 days and payment without retention after a
further 14 days (4.2).

(5) *Statutory obligations*

The requirements for VAT (5.1) and tax deduction regulations
(5.2) to be complied with.

(6) *Insurance*

The contractor indemnifies the employer in respect of personal
injury, death or damage to property other than the Works to the
minimum cover to be stated in the tender (7.1). The employer to
insure existing structures, contents of the Works and unfixed
materials for their full reinstatement value against listed perils
(7.2).

(7) *Determination*

None is provided for, but the employer may cancel the contract
and recover any loss in the event of corruption.

(8) *Supplementary clauses*

There is no provision for water and electricity to be provided by
the employer (to be included in the specification?) nor for access
to the Works by the employer's Representative.

(9) *Settlement of disputes*

Disputes are to be settled by arbitration (not adjudication) (9.1);
if none agreed, to be appointed by the President RICS; the award
to be final and binding (9.2).

Chapter 13

Choosing the appropriate form

Of the three criteria for any building contracts, quality, cost and time, it is unlikely that more than two can be achieved with any precision in any one building project. Cost and time can be saved on a simple commercial project at the cost of quality by using a design/build type of procurement, quality and time at the expense of cost using prime cost or management procedures.

Cost certainty and quality control are achieved providing the time is available to enable the building to be fully designed, with detail drawings and specification prepared, and bills of quantities should they be necessary, prior to the invitation of lump sum tenders. By these means, using consultants and sub-contractors of the client's own choosing and the receipt of tenders on a comparable basis, variations are priced and valuations for interim payments and final accounts accurately prepared; the disadvantage being that a longer period of time is required, because of the need to prepare fully detailed tender documents, before the contractor can start on site, than if the design and build or prime cost and management types of contract were used. Lump sum contracts usually also contain no provision for the acceleration of the progress of the works should the contractor fall behind, and they usually allow for extensions to the contract period should completion be delayed for reasons beyond the control of the contractor. Since these disadvantages were considered not to be outweighed by the advantages of a lump sum tender and the ability to value variations accurately, lump sum tenders were always the preferred option of local authorities and public sector funded projects.

In addition, on the smaller project the time required to complete the design and tender documents was relatively short and for this reason, the shorter standard forms of contract are usually drafted on this basis.

The JCT has issued guidance in a four-page practice note (Practice Note 20) with a two page appendix, detailing the difference between MW 80 and JCT 80 without quantities 'Deciding on the Appropriate Form'.

A guide to contract selection

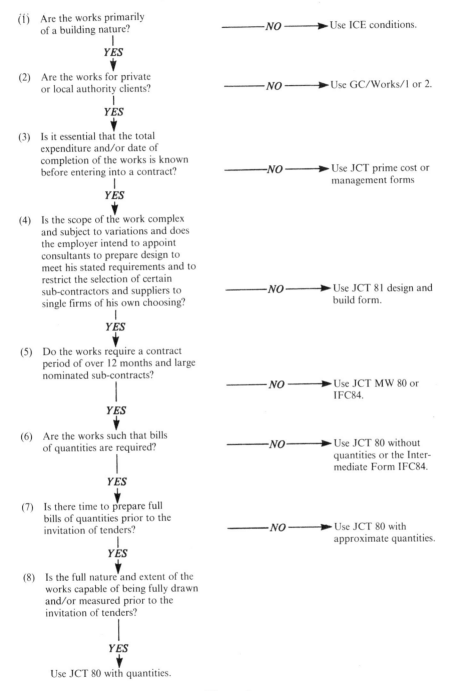

Figure 5

This deals only with the JCT forms they themselves have published for work fully designed by the employer's consultants and obviously leaves out contracts where the whole or a part is designed by the contractor as well as those forms, produced by other bodies, which are discussed elsewhere in this book.

Figure 5 attempts to compensate for these deficiencies. While it is clear that on government contracts GC/Works/1 should be used on contracts in excess of £150,000 and GC/Works/2 on contracts of a lesser value, there is no guidance on the adaptations issued by the Scottish Joint Contracts Committee for the use of forms in Scotland, nor on the JCLI form for use in connection with landscape works. Similarly ASI do not publish guidance on the shorter forms, and it must be left to the judgment of individual architects, engineers and surveyors to decide if the ASI contract better meets their needs or not.

With or without quantities
The question of the inclusion of bills of quantities, prepared by the employer, in the tender and subsequent contract documents is a related but entirely separate matter. The need for bills prepared by the employer arises initially not because the anticipated contract sum exceeds a certain amount (e.g. the £100,000 sum suggested in JCT Practice Note 20), nor because tenderers insist on them (the 1963 *Birmingham Building Trades Employers* case ruled that out – see page 5) but because the employer and his advisers decide that the requirement for comparable tenders, the saving in cost to all tenderers (which may well be reflected in the tenders submitted) and the need for a detailed and accurately priced tender document for the valuation of interim certificates and variations justify the extra expense of the employer having quantities prepared independently.

It is only fair to say at this point that those involved in the building industry in the USA remain unconvinced by this argument, and that several projects have been undertaken in this country of values of £1 million or more for transatlantic employers which have been let on the JCT *without* quantities standard form. Similarly there is no reason why contracts could not be let based on MW 80 but with approximate (non-SMM) quantities provided by the employer, to be confirmed as acceptable by the lowest tenderer prior to contract.

The need to provide quantities, however justified, nevertheless depends on the ability to define the scope of the work, and even if that exists, the time required to prepare completed drawings and specification, and the further time required for the preparation of bills, may make a contract incorporating bills of quantities prepared by the employer impossible.

Traditionally most contracts have existed in separate 'with' and 'without' quantities editions but this is, in reality, quite unnecessary since the inclusion of bills in the contract documents affects less than one per cent of the remaining contract clauses. As long as provision is made in the articles for the optional inclusion of bills as one of the contract documents, then all that remains is to ensure that, where they depart from a standard set of conventions (SMM), the tenderer's attention is drawn to the fact, that any errors in the bill should be allowed for, and that the rates and prices in the 'contract documents' should be used for the valuation of variations and interim certificates.

Contract values

It should be clear therefore that the deciding factor in choosing the most appropriate form must always be the scope and nature of the work and never the amount of the contract sum, nor whether bills of quantities are provided by the employer or not.

The choice of whether bills of quantities or schedules are prepared for the use of tenderers independently on behalf of the employer depends on the type of work to be undertaken. New work best lends itself to bills of quantities measured in accordance with the Standard Method of Measurement, a convention when the minutiae of detail required is appropriate only when the apportionment of the rate between labour and materials conforms to normal circumstances, but which in the case of alterations they rarely do. This is not to say, however, that schedules prepared by an independent quantity surveyor cannot be included in tender documents for alternative contracts.

Any attempts to choose the appropriate form of contract, lump sum or otherwise, solely on the basis of the contract sum is fraught with danger as it over-simplifies the issue and should be strenuously resisted. It is true to say, however, that for *new works* SMM bills of quantities on contracts of a lesser value than £250,000 are rarely justified (at 1990 prices) and for contracts in excess of this they normally are. For *alteration* work quantities are unlikely to be justified for contracts less than this and are probably essential for those in excess of £500,000 (this is of course an architect's view and is unlikely to be acceptable either to a quantity surveyor or a building contractor).

It is worth noting that when MW 68 was published it was suggested as being appropriate for contracts of a value up to £8000 (now thought to be of a jobbing nature only for repairs and minor alterations) and which by the early 1980s was thought to be equivalent to £50,000, then the limit for

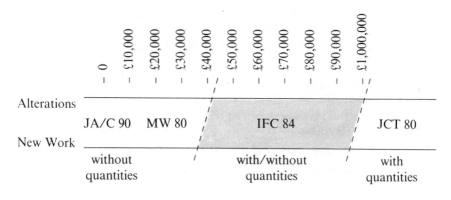

Figure 6

GC/Wks/2 (now (£150,000). Now the use of MW 80 on contracts of up to £150,000 is common, whatever the practice notes may say.

It is therefore clear that there is no distinct line that may be drawn to limit the choice of one of the lump sum contracts or another as Figure 6 attempts to show.

Conclusions

It is hoped that the foregoing has given some guidance as to the principles and intentions of the clauses in the contract conditions of the shorter forms of building contract thereby enabling those entrusted with their administration to exercise their judgment in an informed, fair and equitable manner.

It is also hoped that the signed contract documents will remain in the drawer or on the shelf to which they were consigned at the start of the contract and remain undisturbed, gathering dust until long after the date of the final certificate. This will then enable the participants in the project to devote their energies and enthusiasm to the job itself rather than wrangling over the contractual niceties so that they may turn in due course to the next equally exciting, satisfying and hopefully remunerative project.

Appendix A

The JCT Agreement for Minor Building Works

1·0 Intentions of the parties

Contractor's obligation

1·1 The Contractor shall with due diligence and in a good and workmanlike manner carry out and complete the Works in accordance with the Contract Documents using materials and workmanship of the quality and standards therein specified provided that where and to the extent that approval of the quality of materials or of the standards of workmanship is a matter for the opinion of the Architect/the Contract Administrator such quality and standards shall be to the reasonable satisfaction of the Architect/the Contract Administrator.

Architect's/Contract Administrator's duties

1·2 The Architect/The Contract Administrator shall issue any further information necessary for the proper carrying out of the Works, issue all certificates and confirm all instructions in writing in accordance with these Conditions.

2·0 Commencement and completion

Commencement and completion

2·1 The Works may be commenced on

....

and shall be completed by

....

Extension of contract period

2·2 If it becomes apparent that the Works will not be completed by the date for completion inserted in clause 2·1 hereof (or any later date fixed in accordance with the provisions of this clause 2·2) for reasons beyond the control of the Contractor, including compliance with any instruction of the Architect/the Contract Administrator under this Contract whose issue is not due to a default of the Contractor, then the Contractor shall so notify the Architect/the Contract Administrator who shall make, in writing, such extension of time for completion as may be reasonable. Reasons within the control of the Contractor include any default of the Contractor or of others employed or engaged by or under him for or in connection with the Works and of any supplier of goods or materials for the Works.

Damages for non-completion

2·3 If the Works are not completed by the completion date inserted in clause 2·1 hereof or by any later completion date fixed under clause 2·2 hereof the Contractor shall pay or allow to the Employer liquidated damages at the rate of

£.............................. per .... [b·4] between the aforesaid completion date and the date of practical completion. The Employer may deduct such liquidated damages from any monies due to the Contractor under this Contract or he may recover them from the Contractor as a debt.

Completion date

2·4 The Architect/The Contract Administrator shall certify the date when in his opinion the Works have reached practical completion.

Defects liability

2·5 Any defects, excessive shrinkages or other faults to the Works which appear within three months [c]

....

of the date of practical completion and are due to materials or workmanship not in accordance with the Contract or frost occurring before practical completion shall be made good by the Contractor entirely at his own cost unless the Architect/the Contract Administrator shall otherwise instruct.

The Architect/The Contract Administrator shall certify the date when in his opinion the Contractor's obligations under this clause 2·5 have been discharged.

3·0 Control of the Works

Assignment

3·1 Neither the Employer nor the Contractor shall, without the written consent of the other, assign this Contract.

Sub-contracting

3·2 The Contractor shall not sub-contract the Works or any part thereof without the written consent of the Architect/the Contract Administrator whose consent shall not unreasonably be withheld.

Contractor's representative

3·3 The Contractor shall at all reasonable times keep upon the Works a competent person in charge and any instructions given to him by the Architect/the Contract Administrator shall be deemed to have been issued to the Contractor.

Exclusion from the Works

3·4 The Architect/The Contract Administrator may (but not unreasonably or vexatiously) issue instructions requiring the exclusion from the Works of any person employed thereon.

Architect's/Contract Administrator's instructions

3·5 The Architect/The Contract Administrator may issue written instructions which the Contractor shall forthwith carry out. If instructions are given orally they shall, in two days, be confirmed in writing by the Architect/the Contract Administrator.

If within 7 days after receipt of a written notice from the Architect/the Contract Administrator requiring compliance with an instruction the Contractor does not comply therewith then the Employer may employ and pay other persons to carry out the work and all costs incurred thereby may be deducted by

---

[b·4] Insert 'day', 'week' or other period'.

[c] If a different period is required delete 'three months' and insert the appropriate period.

him from any monies due or to become due to the Contractor under this Contract or shall be recoverable from the Contractor by the Employer as a debt.

Variations

3.6 The Architect/The Contract Administrator may, without invalidating the contract, order an addition to or omission from or other change in the Works or the order or period in which they are to be carried out and any such instruction shall be valued by the Architect/the Contract Administrator on a fair and reasonable basis, using where relevant prices in the priced Specification/schedules/schedule of rates, and such valuation shall include any direct loss and/or expense incurred by the Contractor due to the regular progress of the Works being affected by compliance with such instruction [d].

Instead of the valuation referred to above, the price may be agreed between the Architect/the Contract Administrator and the Contractor prior to the Contractor carrying out any such instruction.

Provisional sums

3.7 The Architect/The Contract Administrator shall issue instructions as to the expenditure of any provisional sums and such instructions shall be valued or the price agreed in accordance with clause 3.6 hereof.

4.0 Payment

Correction of inconsistencies

4.1 Any inconsistency in or between the Contract Drawings [d] and the Contract Specification [d] and the schedules [d] shall be corrected and any such correction which results in an addition, omission or other change shall be treated as a variation under clause 3.6 hereof. Nothing contained in the Contract Drawings [d] or the Contract Specification [d] or the schedules [d] shall override, modify or affect in any way whatsoever the application or interpretation of that which is contained in these Conditions.

Progress payments and retention

4.2 The Architect/The Contract Administrator shall if requested by the Contractor, at intervals of not less than four weeks calculated from the date for commencement, certify progress payments to the Contractor in respect of the value of the Works properly executed, including any amounts either ascertained or agreed under clauses 3.6 and 3.7 hereof, and the value of any materials and goods which have been reasonably and properly brought upon the site for the purpose of the Works and which are adequately stored and protected against the weather and other casualties, less a retention of 5%/...............% [e] and less any previous payments made by the Employer, and the Employer shall pay to the Contractor the amount so certified within 14 days of the date of the certificate.

Penultimate certificate

4.3 The Architect/The Contract Administrator shall within 14 days after the date of practical completion certified under clause 2.4 hereof certify payment to the Contractor of 97½%/...............% [f] of the total amount to be paid to the Contractor under this Contract so far as that amount is ascertainable at the

date of practical completion, including any amounts either ascertained or agreed under clauses 3.6 and 3.7 hereof, less the amount of any progress payments previously made by the Employer, and the Employer shall pay to the Contractor the amount so certified within 14 days of that certificate.

Final certificate

4.4 The Contractor shall supply within three months/

....[g]

from the date of practical completion all documentation reasonably required for the computation of the amount to be finally certified by the Architect/the Contract Administrator and the Architect/the Contract Administrator shall within 28 days of receipt of such documentation, provided that the Architect/the Contract Administrator has issued the certificate under clause 2.5 hereof, issue a final certificate certifying the amount remaining due to the Contractor or due to the Employer as the case may be and such sum shall as from the fourteenth day after the date of the final certificate be a debt payable as the case may be by the Employer to the Contractor or by the Contractor to the Employer.

Contribution, levy and tax changes [h]

4.5 Contribution, levy and tax changes shall be dealt with by the application of Part A of the Supplementary Memorandum to the Agreement for Minor Building Works. The percentage addition under Part A, clause A5 is...............%.

Fixed price

4.6 No account shall be taken in any payment to the Contractor under this Contract of any change in the cost to the Contractor of the labour, materials, plant and other resources employed in carrying out the Works except as provided in clause 4.5 hereof, if applicable.

5.0 Statutory obligations

Statutory obligations, notices, fees and charges

5.1 The Contractor shall comply with, and give all notices required by, any statute, any statutory instrument, rule or order or any regulation or byelaw applicable to the Works (hereinafter called 'the statutory requirements') and shall pay all fees and charges in respect of the Works legally recoverable from him. If the Contractor finds any divergence between the statutory requirements and the Contract Documents or between the statutory requirements and any instruction of the Architect/the Contract Administrator he shall immediately give to the Architect/the Contract Administrator a written

---

[d]   Delete as appropriate to follow any deletions in the recitals on page 1.

[e]   If a different retention is required delete '5%' and insert the appropriate percentage.

[f]   The alternative should be completed where a percentage other than 5% has been inserted in clause 4.2.

[g]   If a different period is required delete 'three months' and insert the appropriate period.

[h]   Delete clause 4.5 if the contract period is of such limited duration as to make the provisions of Part A of the Supplementary Memorandum to this Agreement inapplicable.

notice specifying the divergence. Subject to this latter obligation, the Contractor shall not be liable to the Employer under this Contract if the Works do not comply with the statutory requirements where and to the extent that such non-compliance of the Works results from the Contractor having carried out work in accordance with the Contract Documents or any instruction of the Architect/the Contract Administrator.

Value added tax

5·2 The sum or sums due to the Contractor under Article 2 of this Agreement shall be exclusive of any value added tax and the Employer shall pay to the Contractor any value added tax properly chargeable by the Commissioners of Customs and Excise on the supply to the Employer of any goods and services by the Contractor under this Contract in the manner set out in Part B of the Supplementary Memorandum to the Agreement for Minor Building Works. Clause B1·1 of the Supplementary Memorandum, Part B, applies/does not apply [h·1].

Statutory tax deduction scheme

5·3 Where at the date of tender the Employer was a 'contractor', or where at any time up to the issue and payment of the final certificate the Employer becomes a 'contractor', for the purposes of the statutory tax deduction scheme referred to in Part C of the Supplementary Memorandum to the Agreement for Minor Building Works, Part C of that Memorandum shall be operated.

5·4 [Number not used]

Prevention of corruption

5·5 The Employer shall be entitled to cancel this Contract and to recover from the Contractor the amount of any loss resulting from such cancellation if the Contractor shall have offered or given or agreed to give to any person any gift or consideration of any kind or if the Contractor shall have committed any offence under the Prevention of Corruption Acts 1889 to 1916 or, if the Employer is a local authority, shall have given any fee or reward the receipt of which is an offence under sub-section (2) of section 117 of the Local Government Act 1972 or any re-enactment thereof.

6·0 Injury, damage and insurance

Injury to or death of persons

6·1 The Contractor shall be liable for and shall indemnify the Employer against any expense, liability, loss, claim or proceedings whatsoever arising under any statute or at common law in respect of personal injury to or death of any person whomsoever arising out of or in the course of or caused by the carrying out of the Works, except to the extent that the same is due to any act or neglect of the Employer or of any person for whom the Employer is responsible. Without prejudice to his liability to indemnify the Employer the Contractor shall take out and maintain and shall cause any sub-contractor to take out and maintain insurance which, in respect of liability to employees or apprentices, shall comply with the Employer's Liability (Compulsory Insurance) Act 1969 and any statutory orders made thereunder or any amendment or re-enactment thereof and, in

respect of any other liability for personal injury or death, shall be such as is necessary to cover the liability of the Contractor or, as the case may be, of such sub-contractor.

Injury or damage to property

6·2 The Contractor shall be liable for, and shall indemnify the Employer against, any expense, liability, loss, claim or proceedings in respect of any injury or damage whatsoever to any property real or personal (other than injury or damage to the Works) insofar as such injury or damage arises out of or in the course of or by reason of the carrying out of the Works and to the extent that the same is due to any negligence, breach of statutory duty, omission or default of the Contractor, his servants or agents, or of any person employed or engaged by the Contractor upon or in connection with the Works or any part thereof, his servants or agents. Without prejudice to his obligation to indemnify the Employer the Contractor shall take out and maintain and shall cause any sub-contractor to take out and maintain insurance in respect of the liability referred to above in respect of injury or damage to any property real or personal other than the Works which shall be for an amount not less than the sum stated below for any one occurrence or series of occurrences arising out of one event:

insurance cover referred to above to be not less than:

....

Insurance of the Works – Fire etc. – New Works [i][j·1]

6·3A The Contractor shall in the joint names of Employer and Contractor insure against loss and damage by fire, lightning, explosion, storm, tempest, flood, bursting or overflowing of water tanks, apparatus or pipes, earthquake, aircraft and other aerial devices or articles dropped therefrom, riot and civil commotion for the full reinstatement value thereof plus ....% [k] to cover professional fees, all work executed and all unfixed materials and goods delivered to, placed on or adjacent to the Works and intended therefor.

[h·1] Delete as required. Clause B1·1 can only apply where the Contractor is satisfied at the date the Contract is entered into that his output tax on all supplies to the Employer under the Contract will be at either a positive or a zero rate of tax.

On and from 1 April 1989 the supply in respect of a building designed for a 'relevant residential purpose' or for a 'relevant charitable purpose' (as defined in the legislation which gives statutory effect to the VAT changes operative from 1 April 1989) is only zero rated if the person to whom the supply is made has given to the Contractor a certificate in statutory form: see the VAT leaflet 708 revised 1989. Where a contract supply is zero rated by certificate only the person holding the certificate (usually the Contractor) may zero rate his supply.

[i] Not used.

[j] Delete either 6·3A or 6·3B whichever is not applicable.

[j·1] Where the Contractor has in force an All Risks Policy which insures the Works against loss or damage by *inter alia* the perils referred to in clause 6·3A this Policy may be used to provide the insurance required by clause 6·3A provided the Policy recognises the Employer as a joint insured with the Contractor in respect of the Works and the Policy is maintained.

[k] Percentage to be inserted.

After any inspection required by the insurers in respect of a claim under the insurance mentioned in this clause 6·3A the Contractor shall with due diligence restore or replace work or materials or goods damaged and dispose of any debris and proceed with and complete the Works. The Contractor shall not be entitled to any payment in respect of work or materials or goods damaged or the disposal of any debris other than the monies received under the said insurance (less the percentage to cover professional fees) and such monies shall be paid to the Contractor under certificates of the Architect/the Contract Administrator at the periods stated in clause 4·0 hereof.

Insurance of the Works – Fire etc. – Existing structures [j]

6·3B The Employer shall in the joint names of Employer and Contractor insure against loss or damage to the existing structures (together with the contents owned by him or for which he is responsible) and to the Works and all unfixed materials and goods delivered to, placed on or adjacent to the Works and intended therefor by fire, lightning, explosion, storm, tempest, flood, bursting or overflowing of water tanks, apparatus or pipes, earthquake, aircraft and other aerial devices or articles dropped therefrom, riot and civil commotion.

If any loss or damage as referred to in this clause occurs then the Architect/the Contract Administrator shall issue instructions for the reinstatement and making good of such loss or damage in accordance with clause 3·5 hereof and such instructions shall be valued under clause 3·6 hereof.

Evidence of insurance

6·4 The Contractor shall produce, and shall cause any sub-contractor to produce, such evidence as the Employer may reasonably require that the insurances referred to in clauses 6·1 and 6·2 and, where applicable, 6·3A hereof have been taken out and are in force at all material times. Where clause 6·3B hereof is applicable the Employer shall produce such evidence as the Contractor may reasonably require that the insurance referred to therein has been taken out and is in force at all material times.

7·0 Determination

Determination by Employer

7·1 The Employer may but not unreasonably or vexatiously by notice by registered post or recorded delivery to the Contractor forthwith determine the employment of the Contractor under this Contract if the Contractor shall make default in any one or more of the following respects:

· 1 if the Contractor without reasonable cause fails to proceed diligently with the works or wholly suspends the carrying out of the Works before completion;

· 2 if the Contractor becomes bankrupt or makes any composition or arrangement with his creditors or has a proposal in respect of his company for a voluntary arrangement for a composition of debts or scheme of arrangement approved in accordance with the Insol-

vency Act 1986 or has an application made under the Insolvency Act 1986 in respect of his company to the court for the appointment of an administrator or has a winding up order made or (except for the purposes of reconstruction) a resolution for voluntary winding up passed or a receiver or manager of his business or undertaking duly appointed or has an administrative receiver, as defined in the Insolvency Act 1986, appointed or has possession taken by or on behalf of any creditor of any property the subject of a charge.

In the event of the Employer determining the employment of the Contractor as aforesaid the Contractor shall immediately give up possession of the site of the Works and the Employer shall not be bound to make any further payment to the Contractor until after completion of the Works.

Provided always that the right of determination shall be without prejudice to any other rights or remedies which the Employer may possess.

Determination by Contractor

7·2 The Contractor may but not unreasonably or vexatiously by notice by registered post or recorded delivery to the Employer forthwith determine the employment of the Contractor under this Contract if the Employer shall make default in any one or more of the following respects:

· 1 if the Employer fails to make any progress payment due under the provisions of clause 4·2 hereof within 14 days of such payment being due;

· 2 if the Employer or any person for whom he is responsible interferes with or obstructs the carrying out of the Works or fails to make the premises available for the Contractor in accordance with clause 2·1 hereof;

· 3 if the Employer suspends the carrying out of the Works for a continuous period of at least one month;

· 4 if the Employer becomes bankrupt or makes any composition or arrangement with his creditors or has a proposal in respect of his company for a voluntary arrangement for a composition of debts or scheme of arrangement approved in accordance with the Insolvency Act 1986 or has an application made under the Insolvency Act 1986 in respect of his company to the court for the appointment of an administrator or has a winding up order made or (except for the purposes of reconstruction) a resolution for voluntary winding-up passed or a receiver or manager of his business duly appointed or has an administrative receiver, as defined in the Insolvency Act 1986, appointed or has possession taken by or on behalf of any creditor of any property the subject of a charge.

Provided that the employment of the Contractor shall not be determined under clauses 7·2·1, 7·2·2 or 7·2·3 hereof unless the Employer has continued the default for seven days after receipt by registered post or recorded delivery of a notice from the Contractor specifying such default.

In the event of the Contractor determining the employment of the Contractor as aforesaid the Employer shall pay to the Contractor, after taking into account amounts previously paid, such sum as shall be fair and reasonable for the value of work begun and executed, materials on site and the removal of all temporary buildings, plant, tools and equipment. Provided always that the right of determination shall be without prejudice to any other rights or remedies which the Contractor may possess.

8·0   Supplementary Memorandum

Meaning of references in the 5th recital and 4·5, 5·2 and 5·3

8·1   The references in the 5th recital and clauses 4·5, 5·2 and 5·3 to the Supplementary Memorandum to the Agreement for Minor Building Works are to that issued for use with this Form by the Joint Contracts Tribunal as endorsed hereon.

9·0   Settlement of disputes – Arbitration

9·1   When the Employer or the Contractor require a dispute or difference as referred to in Article 4 to be referred to arbitration then either the Employer or the Contractor shall give written notice to the other to such effect and such dispute or difference shall be referred to the arbitration and final decision of a person to be agreed between the parties as the Arbitrator, or, upon failure so to agree within 14 days after the date of the aforesaid written notice, of a person to be appointed as the Arbitrator on the request of either the Employer or the Contractor by the person named in Article 4.

9·2   Subject to the provisions of clause A4·3 in the Supplementary Memorandum, the Arbitrator shall, without prejudice to the generality of his powers, have power to rectify the Agreement so that it accurately reflects the true agreement made by the Employer and the Contractor, to direct such measurements and/or valuations as may in his opinion be desirable in order to determine the rights of the parties and to ascertain and award any sum which ought to have been the subject of or included in any certificate and to open up, review and revise any certificate, opinion, decision, requirement or notice and to determine all matters in dispute which shall be submitted to him in the same manner as if no such certificate, opinion, decision, requirement or notice had been given.

9·3   The award of such Arbitrator shall be final and binding on the parties.

9·4   If before making his final award the Arbitrator dies or otherwise ceases to act as the Arbitrator, the Employer and the Contractor shall forthwith appoint a further Arbitrator, or, upon failure so to appoint within 14 days of any such death or cessation, then either the Employer or the Contractor may request the person named in Article 4 to appoint such further Arbitrator. Provided that no such further Arbitrator shall be entitled to disregard any direction of the previous Arbitrator or to vary or revise any award of the previous Arbitrator except to the extent that the previous Arbitrator had power so to do under the

JCT Arbitration Rules and/or with the agreement of the parties and/or by the operation of law.

9·5   [I·2] The arbitration shall be conducted in accordance with the 'JCT Arbitration Rules' current at the date of this Agreement [I·1]. Provided that if any amendments to the Rules so current have been issued by the Joint Contracts Tribunal after the aforesaid date the Employer and the Contractor may, by a joint notice in writing to the Arbitrator, state that they wish the arbitration to be conducted in accordance with the JCT Arbitration Rules as so amended.

[I·1]   The JCT Arbitration Rules contain stricter time limits than those prescribed by some arbitration rules or those frequently observed in practice. The parties should note that a failure by a party or the agent of a party to comply with the time limits incorporated in these Rules may have adverse consequences.

[I·2]   Delete clause 9·5 if it is not to apply.

Agreement for Minor Building Works: Supplementary Memorandum

This Memorandum is the Supplementary Memorandum referred to in the Joint Contracts Tribunal's 'Agreement for Minor Building Works', 1980 Edition, the 5th recital and clauses 4·5, 5·2 and 5·3.

Unless otherwise specifically stated words and phrases in the Supplementary Memorandum have the same meaning as in the Agreement for Minor Building Works.

PART A – CONTRIBUTION, LEVY AND TAX CHANGES

Deemed calculation of Contract Sum – rates of contribution etc.

A1 The sum referred to in Article 2 (in this clause called 'the Contract Sum') shall be deemed to have been calculated in the manner set out below and shall be subject to adjustment in the events specified hereunder:

A1·1 The prices used or set out by the Contractor in the Contract Documents are based upon the types and rates of contribution, levy and tax payable by a person in his capacity as an employer and which at the date of the Contract are payable by the Contractor. A type and rate so payable are in clause A1·2 referred to as a 'tender type' and a 'tender rate'.

Increases or decreases in rates of contribution etc. – payment or allowance

A1·2 If any of the tender rates other than a rate of levy payable by virtue of the Industrial Training Act 1964, is increased or decreased, or if a tender type ceases to be payable, or if a new type of contribution, levy or tax which is payable by a person in his capacity as an employer becomes payable after the date of tender,* then in any such case the net amount of the difference between what the Contractor actually pays or will pay in respect of

·1 workpeople* engaged upon or in connection with the Works either on or adjacent to the site of the Works, and

·2 workpeople* directly employed by the Contractor who are engaged upon the production of materials or goods* for use in or in connection with the Works and who operate neither on nor adjacent to the site of the Works and to the extent that they are so engaged

or because of his employment of such workpeople and what he would have paid had the alteration, cessation or new type of contribution, levy or tax not become effective shall, as the case may be, be paid to or allowed by the Contractor.

Persons employed on site other than 'workpeople'

A1·3 There shall be added to the net amount paid to or allowed by the Contractor under clause A1·2 in respect of each person employed on the site by the Contractor for the Works and who is not within the definition of 'workpeople' in clause A4·6·3 the same amount as is payable or allowable in respect of a craftsman under clause A1·2 or such proportion of that amount as reflects the time (measured in whole working days) that each such person is so employed.

A1·4 For the purposes of clause A1·3

no period less than 2 whole working days in any week shall be taken into account and periods less than a whole working day shall not be aggregated to amount to a whole working day;

the phrase 'the same amount as is payable or allowable in respect of a craftsman' shall refer to the amount in respect of a craftsman employed by the Contractor (or by any sub-contractor under a sub-contract to which clause A3 refers) under the rules or decisions or agreements of the National Joint Council for the Building Industry or other wage-fixing body* and, where the aforesaid rules or decisions or agreements provide for more than one rate of wage

emolument or other expense for a craftsman, shall refer to the amount in respect of a craftsman employed as aforesaid to whom the highest rate is applicable; and

the phrase 'employed . . . by the Contractor' shall mean an employment to which the Income Tax (Employment) Regulations 1973 (the PAYE Regulations) under section 204 of the Income and Corporation Taxes Act, 1970, apply.

Refunds and premiums

A1·5 The prices used or set out by the Contractor in the Contract Documents are based upon the types and rates of refund of the contributions, levies and taxes payable by a person in his capacity as an employer and upon the types and rates of premium receivable by a person in his capacity as an employer being in each case types and rates which at the date of tender are receivable by the Contractor. Such a type and such a rate are in clause A1·6 referred to as a 'tender type' and a 'tender rate'.

A1·6 If any of the tender rates is increased or decreased or if a tender type ceases to be payable or if a new type of refund of any contribution levy or tax payable by a person in his capacity as an employer becomes receivable or if a new type of premium receivable by a person in his capacity as an employer becomes receivable after the date of tender, then in any such case the net amount of the difference between what the Contractor actually receives or will receive in respect of workpeople as referred to in clauses A1·2·1 and A1·2·2 or because of his employment of such workpeople and what he would have received had the alteration, cessation or new type of refund or premium not become effective shall, as the case may be, be allowed by or paid to the Contractor.

A1·7 The references in clauses A1·5 and A1·6 to premiums shall be construed as meaning all payments howsoever they are described which are made under or by virtue of an Act of Parliament to a person in his capacity as an employer and which affect the cost to an employer of having persons in his employment.

Contracted-out employment

A1·8 Where employer's contributions are payable by the Contractor in respect of workpeople as referred to in clauses A1·2·1 and A1·2·2 whose employment is contracted-out employment within the meaning of the Social Security Pensions Act 1975 the Contractor shall, for the purpose of recovery or allowance under this clause be deemed to pay employer's contributions as if that employment were not contracted-out employment.

Meaning of contribution etc.

A1·9 The references in clause A1 to contribution, levies and taxes shall be construed as meaning all impositions payable by a person in his capacity as an employer howsoever they are described and whoever the recipient which are imposed under or by virtue of an Act of Parliament and which affect the cost to an employer of having persons in his employment.

Materials – duties and taxes

A2·1 The prices used or set out by the Contractor in the Contract Documents are based upon the types and rates of duty if any and tax if any (other than any value added tax which is treated, or is capable of being treated, as input tax (as

*See clause A4·6.

referred to in the Finance Act 1972) by the Contractor) by whomsoever payable which at the date of tender are payable on the import, purchase, sale, appropriation, processing or use of the materials, goods, electricity and, where so specifically stated in the Contract Documents, fuels specified in the list attached thereto under or by virtue of any Act of Parliament. A type and a rate so payable are in clause A2·2 referred to as a 'tender type' and a 'tender rate'.

A2·2 If in relation to any materials or goods* specified as aforesaid, or any electricity or fuels specified as aforesaid and consumed on site .for the execution of the Works including temporary site installations for those Works, a tender rate is increased or decreased or a tender type ceases to be payable or a new type of duty or tax (other than value added tax which is treated, or is capable of being treated as input tax (as referred to in the Finance Act 1972) by the Contractor) becomes payable on the import, purchase, sale, appropriation, processing or use of those materials, goods, electricity or fuels, then in any such case the net amount of the difference between what the Contractor actually pays in respect of those materials, goods, electricity or fuels (and what he would have paid in respect of them had the alteration, cessation or imposition not occurred, shall, as the case may be, be paid to or allowed by the Contractor. In clause A2 the expression 'a new type of duty or tax' includes an additional duty or tax imposed in regard to specific materials, goods, electricity or fuels in respect of which no duty or tax whatever was previously payable (other than any value added tax which is treated, or is capable of being treated, as input tax (as referred to in the Finance Act 1972) by the Contractor).

Fluctuations – work sublet

A3·1 If the Contractor shall decide to sublet any portion of the Works he shall incorporate in the sub-contract provisions to the like effect as the provisions of

clauses A1, A4 and A5 including the percentage stated in clause 4·5 pursuant to clause A5

which are applicable for the purposes of this Contract.

A3·2 If the price payable under such a sub-contract as aforesaid is decreased below or increased above the price in such sub-contract by reason of the operation of the said incorporated provisions, then the net amount of such decrease or increase shall, as the case may be, be allowed by or paid to the Contractor under this Contract.

Provisions relating to clauses A1, A3 and A5

Written notice by Contractor
A4·1 The Contractor shall give a written notice to the Architect/the Contract Administrator of the occurrence of any of the events referred to in such of the following provisions as are applicable for the purposes of this Contract:
·1 clause A1·2
·2 clause A1·6
·3 clause A2·2
·4 clause A3·2

Timing and effect of written notices
A4·2 Any notice required to be given by the preceding subclause shall be given within a reasonable time after the occurrence of the event to which the notice relates, and the giving of a written notice in that time shall be a condition precedent to any payment being made to the Contractor in respect of the event in question.

Agreement – Architect/Contract Administrator and Contractor
A4·3 The Architect/The Contract Administrator and the Contractor may agree what shall be deemed for all the

purposes of this Contract to be the net amount payable to or allowable by the Contractor in respect of the occurrence of any event such as is referred to in any of the provisions listed in clause A4·1.

Fluctuations added to or deducted from Contract Sum – provisions setting out conditions etc. to be fulfilled before such addition or deduction
A4·4 Any amount which from time to time becomes payable to or allowable by the Contractor by virtue of clause A1 or clause A3 shall, as the case may be, be added to or deducted from the Contract Sum:

Provided:

– evidence by Contractor –
·1 As soon as is reasonably practicable the Contractor shall provide such evidence as the Architect/the Contract Administrator may reasonably require to enable the amount payable to or allowable by the Contractor by virtue of clause A1 or clause A3 to be ascertained; and in the case of amounts payable to or allowable by the sub-contractor under clause A4·1·3 (or clause A3 for amounts payable to or allowable by the sub-contractor under provisions in the sub-contract to the like effect as clauses A1·3 and A1·4) – employees other than workpeople – such evidence shall include a certificate signed by or on behalf of the Contractor each week certifying the validity of the evidence reasonably required to ascertain such amounts.

– actual payment by Contractor –
·2 No amount shall be included in or deducted from the amount which would otherwise be stated as due in progress payments by virtue of this clause unless on or before the date as at which the total value of work, materials and goods is ascertained for the purposes of any progress payment the Contractor shall have actually paid or received the sum which is payable by or to him in consequence of the event in respect of which the payment or allowance arises.

– no alteration to Contractor's profit –
·3 No addition to or subtraction from the Contract Sum made by virtue of this clause shall alter in any way the amount of profit of the Contractor included in that Sum.

– position where Contractor in default over completion –
·4·1 No amount shall be included in or deducted from the amount which would otherwise be stated as due in progress payments or in the final certificate in respect of amounts otherwise payable to or allowable by the Contractor by virtue of clause A1 or clause A3 if the event (as referred to in the provisions listed in clause A4·1) in respect of which the payment or allowance would be made occurs after the completion date fixed under clause 2.

·4·2 Clause A4·4·4·1 shall not operate unless:
·1 the printed text of clause 25 is unamended; and
·2 the Architect/the Contract Administrator has, in respect of every written notification by the Contractor under clause 2 of the Agreement fixed such completion date as he considered to be in accordance with that clause.

Work etc. to which clauses A1 and A3 not applicable
A4·5 Clause A1 and Clause A3 shall not apply in respect of:

·1 work for which the Contractor is allowed daywork rates in accordance with any such rates included in the Contract Documents;

·2 changes in the rate of value added tax charged on the supply of goods or services by the Contractor to the Employer under this Contract.

---

*See clause A4·6.

Definitions for use with clause A1

A4·6   In clause A1:

·1   the expression 'the date of tender' means the date 10 days before the date when the Agreement is executed by the parties;

·2   the expressions 'materials' and 'goods' include timber used in formwork but do not include other consumable stores, plant and machinery except electricity and, where specifically so stated in the Contract Documents, fuels;

·3   the expression 'workpeople' means persons whose rates of wages and other emoluments (including holiday credits) are governed by the rules or decisions or agreements of the National Joint Council for the Building Industry or some other wage-fixing body for trades associated with the building industry;

·4   the expression 'wage-fixing body' means a body which lays down recognised terms and conditions of workers within the meaning of the Employment Protection Act 1975, Schedule 11 paragraph 2(a).

Percentage addition to fluctuation payments or allowances

A5   There shall be added to the amount paid to or allowed by the Contractor under:
·1   clause A1·2
·2   clause A1·3
·3   clause A1·6
·4   clause A2·2
the percentage stated in clause 4·5

PART B – VALUE ADDED TAX

B1   In this clause 'VAT' means the value added tax introduced by the Finance Act 1972 which is under the care and management of the Commissioners of Customs and Excise (hereinafter called 'the Commissioners').

B1·1   ·1   Where in clause 5·2 it is stated that clause B1·1 applies clauses B2·1 and B2·2 hereof shall not apply unless and until any notice issued under clause B1·1·4 hereof becomes effective or unless the Contractor fails to give the written notice required under clause B1·1·2. Where clause B1·1 applies clauses B1 and B3·1 to B10 inclusive remain in full force and effect.

·2   Not later than 7 days before the date for the issue of the first certificate under clause 4·2 the Contractor shall give written notice to the Employer, with a copy to the Architect/the Contract Administrator, of the rate of tax chargeable on the supply of goods and services for which certificates under clauses 4·2 and 4·3 and the final certificate under clause 4·4 are to be issued. If the rate of tax so notified is varied under statute the Contractor shall, not later than 7 days after the date when such varied rate comes into effect, send to the Employer, with a copy to the Architect/the Contract Administrator, the necessary amendment to the rate given in his written notice and that notice shall then take effect as so amended.

·3   For the purpose of complying with clause 5·2 for the payment by the Employer to the Contractor of tax properly chargeable by the Commissioners on the Contractor, an amount calculated at the rate given in the aforesaid written notice (or, where relevant, amended written notice) shall be shown on each certificate issued by the Architect/the Contract Administrator under clauses 4·2 and 4·3 and, unless the procedure set out in clause B3 hereof shall have been completed, on the final certificate issued by the Architect/the Contract Administrator under clause 4·4.

Such amount shall be paid by the Employer to the Contractor or by the Contractor to the Employer as the case may be within the period for payment of certificates given in clauses 4·2, 4·3 and 4·4.

·4   Either the Employer or the Contractor may give written notice to the other, with a copy to the Architect/the Contract Administrator, stating that with effect from the date of the notice clause B1·1 shall no longer apply. From that date the provisions of clauses B2·1 and B2·2 shall apply in place of clause B1·1 hereof.

B2·1   Unless clause B1·1 applies the Architect/the Contract Administrator shall inform the Contractor of the amount certified under clause 4·2 and immediately the Contractor shall give to the Employer a written provisional assessment of the respective values of those supplies of goods and services for which the certificate is being issued and which will be chargeable at the relevant times of supply on the Contractor at any rate or rates of VAT (including zero). The Contractor shall also specify the rate or rates of VAT which are chargeable on those supplies.

B2·2   Upon receipt of the Contractor's written provisional assessment the Employer shall calculate the amount of VAT due by applying the rate or rates of VAT specified by the Contractor to the amount of the supplies included in his assessment, and shall remit the calculated amount of such VAT to the Contractor when making payment to him of the amount certified by the Architect/the Contract Administrator under clause 4·2.

B3·1   Where clause B1·1 is operated clause B3 only applies if no amount of tax pursuant to clause B1·1·3 has been shown on the final certificate issued by the Architect/the Contract Administrator. After the issue by the Architect/the Contract Administrator of his certificate of making good defects under clause 2·5 of the Agreement the Contractor shall, as soon as he can finally so ascertain, prepare and submit to the Employer a written final statement of the value of all supplies of goods and services for which certificates have been or will be issued which are chargeable on the Contractor at any rate or rates of VAT (including zero). The Contractor shall also specify the rate or rates of VAT which are chargeable on those supplies and shall state the grounds on which he considers such supplies are so chargeable. He shall also state the total amount of VAT already received by him.

B3·2   Upon receipt of the written final statement the Employer shall calculate the amount of VAT due by applying the rate or rates of VAT specified by the Contractor to the value of the supplies included in the statement and deducting therefrom the total amount of VAT already received by the Contractor and shall pay the balance of such VAT to the Contractor within 28 days from receipt of the statement.

B3·3   If the Employer finds that the total amount of VAT specified in the final statement as already paid by him exceeds the amount of VAT calculated under clause B3·2 he shall so notify the Contractor, who shall refund such excess to the Employer within 28 days of receipt of the notification together with a receipt under clause B4 hereof showing a correction of the amounts for which a receipt or receipts have previously been issued by the Contractor.

B4   Upon receipt of any VAT properly paid under the provisions of this clause the Contractor shall issue to the Employer an authenticated receipt of the kind referred to in Regulation 12(4) of the Value Added Tax (General) Regulations 1985 or any amendment or re-enactment thereof.

B5·1   In calculating the amount of VAT to be paid to the Contractor under clauses B2 and B3 hereof, the Employer shall disregard any sums which the Contractor may be liable to pay or allow to the Employer, or which the Employer may deduct, under clause 2·3 as liquidated damages.

B5·2   The Contractor shall likewise disregard such liquidated damages when stating the value of supplies of goods or services in his written final statement under clause B3·1.

B5·3   Where clause B1·1 is operated the Employer shall pay the tax to which that clause refers notwithstanding any deduction which the Employer may be empowered to make by clause 2·3 from monies due to the Contractor under certificates for payment issued by the Architect/the Contract Administrator.

B6·1   If the Employer disagrees with the final statement issued by the Contractor under clause B3·1 he may request the Contractor to obtain the decision of the Commissioners on the VAT properly chargeable on the Contractor for all supplies of goods and services under this Contract and the Contractor shall forthwith request the Commissioners for such decision.

B6·2   If the Employer disagrees with such decision, then, provided he secures the Contractor against all costs and other expenses, the Contractor shall in accordance with the instructions of the Employer make all such appeals against the decision of the Commissioners as the Employer may request.

B6·3   Within 21 days of the date of the decision of the Commissioners (or of the final adjudication of an appeal) the Employer or the Contractor, as the case may be, shall pay or refund to the other any VAT underpaid or overpaid in accordance with such decision or adjudication. The Contractor shall also account to the Employer for any costs awarded in his favour. The provisions of clause B3·3 shall apply in regard to the provision of authenticated receipts.

B7   The provisions of Article 4 (arbitration) shall not apply to any matters to be dealt with under clause B6.

B8   If any dispute or difference between the Employer and the Contractor is referred to an Arbitrator appointed under clause 9 or to a Court, then insofar as any payment awarded in such arbitration or court proceedings varies amounts certified for payment of goods or services supplied by the Contractor to the Employer under this Contract or is an amount which ought to have been but was not so certified, then the provisions of this Part B shall so far as relevant and applicable apply to any such payments.

B9   Notwithstanding any provisions to the contrary elsewhere in the Agreement the Employer shall not be obliged to make any further payment to the Contractor if the Contractor is in default in providing the receipt referred to in clause B4; provided that this clause B9 shall only apply where

      the Employer can show that he requires such receipt to validate any claim for credit for tax paid or payable under this Part B which the Employer is entitled to make to the Commissioners and

      the Employer has paid tax in accordance with the provisional assessment of the Contractor under clause B2·2 or paid tax in accordance with clause B1·1.

B10   The Employer shall be discharged from any further liability to pay tax to the Contractor under the clause upon payment of tax in accordance either with clause B3·2 (adjusted where relevant in accordance with the decision in any appeal to which clause B6 refers) or with clause B1·1·3 in respect of the tax shown in the final certificate. Provided always that if after the due discharge under clause B10 the Commissioners decide to correct the tax due from the Contractor on the supply to the Employer of any goods and services by the Contractor under this Contract the amount of such correction shall be an additional payment by the Employer to the Contractor or by the Contractor to the Employer as the case may be. The provisions of clause B6 in regard to

disagreement with any decision of the Commissioners shall apply to any decision referred to in this proviso.

PART C – STATUTORY TAX DEDUCTION SCHEME – FINANCE (No.2) ACT 1975 [a]

C1 In this clause 'the Act' means the Finance (No.2) Act 1975 as amended by the Finance Act 1980; 'the Regulations' means the Income Tax (Sub-Contractors in the Construction Industry) Regulations 1985 S.I. No.1960 as amended by S.I. 1980 No.1135, and the Income Tax (Construction Operations) Order 1980 S.I. No.171; "'contractor'" means a person who is a contractor for the purposes of the Act and the Regulations; 'evidence' means such evidence as is required by the Regulations to be produced to a 'contractor' for the verification of a 'sub-contractor's' tax certificate; 'statutory deduction' means the deduction referred to in section 69(4) of the Act or such other deduction as may be in force at the relevant time; "'sub-contractor'" means a person who is a sub-contractor for the purposes of the Act and the Regulations; 'tax certificate' is a certificate issuable under section 70 of the Act.

Provision of evidence – tax certificate

C2·1 Not later than 21 days before the first payment becomes due under clause 4 or after the Employer becomes a contractor as referred to in clause 5·3 the Contractor shall:

either

·1 provide the Employer with the evidence that the Contractor is entitled to be paid without the statutory deduction;

or

·2 inform the Employer in writing, and send a duplicate copy to the Architect/the Contract Administrator, that he is not entitled to be paid without the statutory deduction.

C2·2 If the Employer is not satisfied with the validity of the evidence submitted in accordance with clause C2·1·1 hereof, he shall within 14 days of the Contractor submitting such evidence notify the Contractor in writing that he intends to make the statutory deduction from payments due under this Contract to the Contractor who is a 'sub-contractor' and give his reasons for that decision. The Employer shall at the same time comply with clause C5·1.

Uncertificated Contractor obtains tax certificate

C3·1 Where clause C2·1·2 applies, the Contractor shall immediately inform the Employer if he obtains a tax certificate and thereupon clause C2·1·1 shall apply.

Expiry of tax certificate

C3·2 If the period for which the tax certificate has been issued to the Contractor expires before the final payment is made to the Contractor under this Contract the Contractor shall, not later than 28 days before the date of expiry:

either

·1 provide the Employer with evidence that the Contractor from the said date of expiry is entitled to be paid for a further period without the statutory deduction in which case the provisions of clause C2·2 hereof shall apply if the Employer is not satisfied with the evidence;

or

·2 inform the Employer in writing that he will not be entitled to be paid without the statutory deduction after the said date of expiry.

Cancellation of tax certificate

C3·3 The Contractor shall immediately inform the Employer in writing if his current tax certificate is cancelled and give the date of such cancellation.

Vouchers

C4 The Employer shall, as a 'contractor', in accordance with the Regulations, send promptly to the Inland Revenue any voucher which, in compliance with the Contractor's obligations as a 'sub-contractor' under the Regulations, the Contractor gives to the Employer.

Statutory deduction – direct cost of materials

C5·1 If at any time the Employer is of the opinion (whether because of the information given under clause C2·1·2 or of the expiry or cancellation of the Contractor's tax certificate or otherwise) that he will be required by the Act to make a statutory deduction from any payment due to be made the Employer shall immediately so notify the Contractor in writing and require the Contractor to state not later than 7 days before each future payment becomes due (or within 10 days of such notification if that is later) the amount to be included in such payment which represents the direct cost to the Contractor and any other person of materials used or to be used in carrying out the Works.

C5·2 Where the Contractor complies with clause C5·1 he shall indemnify the Employer against loss or expense caused to the Employer by any incorrect statement of the amount of direct cost referred to in that clause.

C5·3 Where the contractor does not comply with clause C5·1 the Employer shall be entitled to make a fair estimate of the amount of direct cost referred to in that clause.

Correction of errors

C6 Where any error or omission has occurred in calculating or making the statutory deduction the Employer shall correct that error or omission by repayment to, or by deduction from payments to, the Contractor as the case may be subject only to any statutory obligation on the Employer not to make such correction.

Relation to other clauses of Agreement

C7 If compliance with this clause involves the Employer or the Contractor in not complying with any other provisions of the Agreement, then the provisions of this clause shall prevail.

Application of arbitration agreement

C8 The provisions of Article 4 (arbitration) shall apply to any dispute or difference between the Employer or the Architect/the Contract Administrator on his behalf and the Contractor as to the operation of this clause except where the Act or the Regulations or any other Act of Parliament provide for some other method of resolving such dispute or difference.

PART D – not used

---

[a] The application of the Tax Deduction Scheme and these provisions is explained in JCT Practice Note 8 (1980).

PART E – AMENDMENTS FOR USE WHERE THE 5TH RECITAL APPLIES: APPLICATION OF A GUARANTEE/ WARRANTY SCHEME IN RESPECT OF THE WORKS

Section 1: Application of Building Employers Confederation ('BEC') Guarantee Scheme ('the BEC Scheme') operated by BEC Building Trust Limited ('the Company')

E1·1 The Recitals shall include the following additional recital:

6th The Employer has received the documents (the 'Scheme Documents', reference GS/9A) which set out the rights of the Employer and the obligations of the Contractor and the Company under the BEC Guarantee Scheme for small building works where an Architect/a Contract Administrator has been appointed on behalf of the Employer.

E1·2 The BEC Scheme and the modifications to the Agreement set out in clauses E1·4 to E1·8 inclusive shall only apply to this Agreement at and from the date when the Company has confirmed to the Employer by its Registration Certificate issued to the Employer that the Agreement has been registered by the Company. At and from such date the Employer and Contractor agree to abide by the provisions of the Scheme Documents.

E1·3 The Employer may by notice in writing to the Contractor rescind the Agreement within 14 days of the date if any notification to him by the Company that the Agreement has not been registered by the Company. Upon such rescission the Employer shall be discharged from any obligations under the Agreement.

E1·4 The defects liability period in clause 2·5 of the Agreement shall be six months.

E1·5 The Employer shall himself send, or arrange for the Architect/the Contract Administrator to send, to the Company a copy of the certificate of practical completion and of the final certificate.

E1·6 Clause 6·3A and clause 6·4 of the Agreement shall not apply.

E1·7 The following provisions shall apply in respect of the insurance of the existing structures in place of clause 6·3B of the Agreement:

·1 Where the Works are in, or are an extension to, an existing structure the Employer shall in the joint names of the Employer and the Contractor insure against loss or damage to the existing structures (together with the contents owned by him or for which he is responsible) by fire, lightning, explosion, storm, tempest, flood, bursting or overflowing of water tanks, apparatus or pipes, earthquake, aircraft and other aerial devices or articles dropped therefrom, riot and civil commotion.

·2 The Employer shall produce such evidence as the Contractor may reasonably require that the insurance referred to in clause E1·7·1 has been taken out and is in force at all material times.

E1·8 The following provisions shall apply in respect of loss or damage to the Works and insurance for such loss or damage [j]:

·1 From the date of registration of the Agreement by the Company, the Contractor shall ensure that the Company provides in the joint names of the Employer and the Contractor insurance, whose terms are set out in the Scheme Documents,

against loss or damage to all work executed and all unfixed materials and goods intended for, delivered to and placed on or adjacent to the Works and

for the professional fees involved in the restoration or replacement of work or materials or goods so lost or damaged.

·2 The Contractor shall produce such evidence as the Employer may reasonably require that the insurance referred to in clause E1·8·1 has been effected and is in force at all material times.

·3 After any inspection required by the insurers in respect of a claim under the insurance referred to in clause E1·8·1 the Contractor shall with due diligence restore or replace work or materials or goods damaged and dispose of any debris and proceed with and complete the Works.

·4 The Contractor shall not be entitled to any payment in respect of work or materials or goods damaged or the disposal of any debris other than the monies received under the said insurance excluding any monies paid by the insurers in respect of any professional fees incurred by the Employer in connection with the restoration or replacement of work or materials or goods lost or damaged.

---

[j] As this insurance against loss or damage to the Works and materials and goods is effective only from the date of registration of the Agreement by the Company work should not be commenced nor should materials or goods be delivered to or placed on or adjacent to the Works before that date.

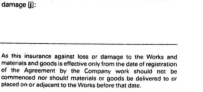

Appendix B

Form of tender and conditions of sub-contract

This form has been prepared by the author for use in his own office with JCT MW 80 for domestic and named sub-contractors. Readers should ensure that it meets their own requirements and if necessary take legal advice before adopting it.

INFORMATION FOR TENDERERS

1. Contract name and location: ....

2. Employer: ....

3. Contractor: ....

4. Architect/Supervising Officer: ....

5. The Form of Contract is the JCT Agreement for Minor Building Works 1980, completed as follows:

Clause 2.1: The Works may be commenced on .... and shall be completed by ....

Clause 2.3: Liquidated damages: £ .... per week or part of a week.

Clause 2.5: Defects Liability Period: ...... months.

*Clause 6.3A will be deleted.

*Clause 6.3B will be deleted, the insurance under clause 6.3A being the full value plus ...... %

6. The Subcontractor shall, before tendering, visit the Site or otherwise make himself familiar with the extent of the Subcontract Works, the Site Conditions, and all local conditions and restrictions likely to affect the execution of the work. The Subcontractor may have access to any available drawings or work programmes relative to the preparation of his tender on request and by appointment.

7. Two copies of this Form are provided – one copy to be priced, signed by the Subcontractor and returned to .... , the other is for his retention.

FORM OF TENDER

1. Tender price for ....
   (The Enquirer should enter trade or brief description of Works)
   .... Total tender price.
   The Tenderer should enter the amount of his tender in words and figures.

2a   The tender is to be adjusted for price fluctuations of labour only/materials only*/ labour and materials* as set out in Subcontract Condition 4.4, a list of relevant basic prices being enclosed.

2b   The tender is to be adjusted for price fluctuations by use of the NEDO Price Adjustment Formula Indices (Category ....)/the Specialist Engineering Installation Indices (Category ....)*.

*2c   The tender is to be on a firm price basis.

3.   Schedule of Daywork Charges
The Subcontractor is requested to insert his hourly daywork rates in the space provided in the Schedule below. His rates for labour shall be deemed to include overheads and profit and all payments in connection with Holidays with Pay, Bonus and Pension Schemes, Subsistence Allowances, Fares and Travelling Time, Imported Labour Costs, Non-Productive Overtime Costs, and any other payments made under the Working Rule Agreement, any Regulation; Bye-law or Act of Parliament. The Subcontractor is also invited to insert in the space provided the percentage addition he will require for his overheads and profits on the nett cost of materials and on plant charges.

(i)   Labour

    Craftsmen @ .... £......... per hour
    Labourers/Mates @ .... £......... per hour
(ii) Materials and Plant

    Materials invoice cost plus .... %
    Plant Charges plus .... %

4.   Period of notice required before commencing the Subcontract Works: ....
Time required to complete the Subcontract Works (the Subcontract Period unless agreed otherwise): ....

5.   We, the undersigned, agree that this quotation will be open for acceptance within .... week(s) and that we have read and understand the terms and conditions printed overleaf and that should our quotation be accepted we will enter into a Subcontract in accordance with the said terms and conditions.

    For and on behalf of ....
                          ....

Signed .... Date ....

* Delete if not required.

CONDITIONS OF SUBCONTRACT

1.0   INTENTIONS

1.1   Subcontractor's obligation
The Subcontractor shall with due diligence and in a good and workmanlike manner carry out and complete the Works in accordance with the Subcontract Documents using materials and workmanship of the quality and standards therein specified provided that where and to the extent that approval of the quality of materials or of the standards of workmanship is a matter for the opinion of the Architect/Supervising Officer such quality and standards shall be to the reasonable satisfaction of the Architect/Supervising Officer.
No approval expressed or implied by the Contractor, the Architect/Supervising Officer shall in any way relieve the Subcontractor of his responsibility for complying with the requirements of this Subcontract.

1.2 Principal Contract and special conditions

The Subcontractor is deemed to have full knowledge of, and so far as they are applicable to the Works agrees to comply with, the provisions of the Principal Contract as though the same were incorporated herein and the Contractor were the Employer and the Subcontractor were the Contractor. Any conditions contained in the Subcontractor's Tender shall be excluded.

1.3 Information provided by others

The Subcontractor must make written application to the Contractor for instructions, drawings, levels or other information at a date which is not unreasonably distant from nor unreasonably close to the date on which it is necessary for the Subcontractor to receive the same.

1.4 Information provided for others

Any instructions, drawings, levels or other information relating to the Works which is requested from the Subcontractor must be provided in due time and so as not to cause disruption or delay to the works to be performed under the Principal Contract.

2.0 COMMENCEMENT AND COMPLETION

2.1 Progress and completion

The Works are to be commenced within the period of notice stated on the Form of Tender and are to be completed within the Subcontract period subject only to such fair and reasonable extension of time as the Contractor shall allow. The Works are to be carried out diligently and in such order, manner and time as the Contractor may reasonably direct so as to ensure completion of the Principal Contract Works or any portion thereof by the completion date or such extended date as may be allowed under the Principal Contract. If the Subcontractor is in breach of the foregoing he shall pay or allow to the Contractor the amount of loss or damage suffered by the Contractor in consequence thereof.

2.2 Overtime

No overtime is to be worked without the Subcontractor first obtaining the consent in writing of the Contractor. No additional payment for overtime will be made unless the Subcontractor is so advised in writing by the Contractor and, if the Subcontractor is so advised, he will be reimbursed the net additional non-productive rate incurred, including any net additional cost of Employers' Liability and Third Party Insurances. The Subcontractor will be required to obtain any necessary overtime permit from the appropriate authority.

2.3 Annual holidays

Under the Annual Holiday Agreement, the Site will be closed down for certain periods which may be whilst the Subcontractor's work is in progress. The Subcontractor will be deemed to have included in his Tender for any additional costs and time resulting from such closure.

2.4 Maintenance and defects liability

The Subcontractor will (a) maintain the Works at his own expense to the Contractor's and the Architect Supervising Officer's satisfaction both during the progress of the Works and until the Architect Supervising Officer has issued a Certificate of Practical Completion including the Works and (b) make good at his own expense, and at a time to be decided by the Contractor, any defects or damage to the Works.

3.0 CONTROL OF THE WORKS

3.1 Assignment

Neither the Contractor nor the Subcontractor shall, without the written consent of the other, assign this Contract.

3.2 Use of site

The Site shall not be used for any purpose other than for the carrying out of the Works. Works to be executed outside the Main Contractor's Site boundary shall be carried out to suit the convenience of adjacent occupiers or Local Authorities at times to be agreed by the Contractor in writing.

3.3 Variations

No variation shall vitiate this Subcontract. The Subcontractor shall advise the Contractor in writing of all work involving a variation or extra work within 14 days of such variation or extra work becoming apparent, at the same time submitting detailed and priced calculations based upon this Subcontract showing such price adjustment, if any. Variations or extra work shall not be undertaken by the Subcontractor nor shall he receive payment for such variation or extra works without written authority from the Contractor.

Where variations or extra works cannot be valued by reference to this Subcontract then the value of such variations or extra works shall be subject to agreement between the Contractor and/or the Architect/Supervising Officer and the Subcontractor.

3.4 Dayworks

No daywork will be permitted except where in the opinion of the Contractor and/or the Architect/Supervising Officer, it would be unfair to value such work at other than daywork rates. Where the Subcontractor considers he has claim to daywork due notice must be given and valuation by daywork approved by the Contractor in writing prior to the execution of the work in question in order to facilitate checking the time and materials expended thereon. All daywork sheets shall be rendered by the end of the week during which the work is executed. All daywork will be paid for at the rates stated on the Form of Tender.

3.5 Adjustment for provisional sums

Instructions will be issued in respect of Provisional Sums. No loss of profit will be allowed in respect of such instructions.

4.0 PAYMENT

4.1 Discount to the contractor

The Subcontractor will allow for all payments to be made in full within 17 days of the date of the Architect's Certificate to the Employer without any cash discount for prompt payment. Any such discount included on the Form of Tender will be deducted from the tender sum before the order for the subcontract works is placed.

4.2 Progress payments

Payment will, subject always to these terms and conditions, be made to the Subcontractor as and when the value of such Works under the terms of the Principal Contract is included in a Certificate to the Contractor and the Contractor receives the monies due thereunder. Applications for payment are to be rendered to the Contractor in duplicate by the Subcontractor.
Payment shall be by instalments of the rate of:

95% of the value executed as the Works proceed.
$2\frac{1}{2}$% upon practical completion of the Works.

$2\frac{1}{2}$% on satisfactory completion of making good defects under the Principal Contract or as soon as the final account for all Works executed under this Subcontract shall have been agreed, whichever may last happen.

Progress payments shall be on account only and shall not be held to signify approval by the Contractor and/or the Architect/Supervising Officer of the whole or any part of the Works executed nor shall any final payment prejudice any claim the Contractor may have in respect of any defects in the Works whenever such defects may appear.

4.3 Estimates of loss, etc

In addition to the Contractor's Common Law rights of set off, if the Subcontractor shall cause the Contractor loss by reason of any breach of this Contract or by any tortious act or by any breach of statutory duty giving rise to a claim for damages or indemnity or contribution by the Contractor against the Subcontractor, or the Contractor shall become entitled to payment from the Subcontractor under this Contract, then without prejudice to and pending the final determination or agreement between the parties, the Contractor shall bona fide estimate the amount of such loss, indemnity or contribution or payment, such estimate to be binding and conclusive upon the Subcontractor until such final determination or agreement.

4.4 Fluctuations (to apply only if item 2a of the Form of Tender is completed)

The sum or sums referred to in this Subcontract shall be based upon the rates of wages and such other emoluments, allowances and expenses (including the cost of Employers' Liability and Third Party Insurances) as are properly payable by the Subcontractor to work-people engaged upon or in connection with the Works in accordance with the rules or decisions of the wage fixing body of the trade or trades concerned applicable to the Works. Such rates of wages and the prices of materials shall be as detailed in the Basic Price List as provided by the Subcontractor and attached hereto.

Should any fluctuations from the Basic Price List occur during the currency of this Subcontract, the net additional cost actually and properly incurred or saving that ought to have been made, by such fluctuations shall be added to or be deducted from the total amount payable under the terms and conditions of this Subcontract. Fluctuations in the cost of materials will be adjusted net.

Provided always that immediate notice in writing shall be given of such fluctuations, and an approved weekly return submitted to the Contractor showing the total number of men and hours and the deliveries of materials effected for detailed checking by the Contractor and Architect/Supervising Officer.

5.0 STATUTORY OBLIGATIONS

5.1 Safety, Health and Welfare
The Subcontractor shall comply with the Contractor's requirements on matters affecting the safe conduct of work on the Site and all statutes, bye-laws and regulations affecting the Works and the carrying out thereof.

5.2 Statutory payments
The Subcontractor shall include in his quotation for any payments to be made under the Working Rule Agreement, all payments in connection with holidays with Pay, Bonus and Pension Schemes, National Insurance, Subsistence Allowances, Fares and Travelling Time, Imported Labour Costs or any payments required by Regulations, Bye-law or Act of Parliament.

6.0 INJURY, DAMAGE AND INSURANCE

6.1 Responsibilities of the Subcontractor
The Subcontractor shall indemnify the Contractor against all claims, causes of action, costs, loss and expense whatsoever in respect of:

1.   Personal injury or death of any person or injury or damage to any property real or personal arising out of or in the course of or caused by any works executed by the Subcontractor and/or the execution of such works (including but not restricted to the use of any plant, equipment or facilities whether in connection with such execution or otherwise) and/or any design (undertaken) by the Subcontractor and

2.   Any negligence or breach of duty on the part of the Subcontractor, his Subcontractors, his or their servants or agents and

3.   Any breach or non-performance or non-observance by the Subcontractor, his Subcontractors, his or their servants or agents of the provisions of the Principal Contract in so far as they relate or apply to the Works and are not inconsistent with the provisions of this Subcontract.

4.   Any act, omission, default or neglect of the Subcontractor, his Subcontractors, his or their servants or agents which involves the Contractor in any liability under the Principal Contract.

5.   Any damage, claim, loss or expense to or involving any plant (whether of the type aforesaid or otherwise) hired or loaned or otherwise made available to the Subcontractor or operating for the Subcontractor's benefit.

6.2 Responsibilities of others
The Subcontractor shall not be responsible for loss or damage caused by fire, storm, tempest,

lightning, flood, bursting and overflowing of water tanks, apparatus or pipes, earthquake, aircraft or anything dropped therefrom, aerial objects, riot and civil commotion, to the Works or to any materials (other than temporary buildings, plant, tools, scaffolding and machinery provided by the Subcontractor, or any scaffolding or other plant which is loaned to him by the Contractor), properly upon the Site and in connection with and for the purpose of the Subcontract. In the event of any such loss or damage, the Subcontractor shall, if and when directed by the Contractor in writing, proceed immediately with the rectification or replacement of the damaged work and materials and the erection and completion of the Works in full accordance with the terms, provisions and conditions hereof, and expenses in respect of any of the matters referred to in sub-clause 6.1.1 and 6.12 above and shall on demand produce to the Contractor adequate evidence of such insurance.

6.3 Subcontractor's work, materials and plant
The Works, materials, tools, plant scaffolding, machinery and buildings of the Subcontractor, the subject of or used in connection with this Subcontract whether on Site or not, shall in every respect be at the Subcontractor's risk (except those risks for which the Subcontractor is not responsible under Clause 6.2).

6.4 Subcontractor's insurance
The Subcontractor shall adequately insure:
  (a) His and the Contractor's liability in respect of any claims, causes of action, costs, losses and expenses in respect of any of the matters referred to in sub-clauses 6.1(1.) and (2.) above.
  (b) Against all Employers' Liability and Third Party (including Third Party Fire) risks arising out of the execution of the Works.
The Subcontractor shall produce on demand policies of such insurances, together with receipts for premiums, or other adequate evidence of such insurance.

In case of neglect by the Subcontractor to effect the insurances, the Contractor shall be at liberty to insure on behalf of the Subcontractor and to deduct the premium so paid from any monies due or becoming due to the Subcontractor.

7.0 DETERMINATION

7.1 Determination by the Contractor
The Contractor may without prejudice to any other of his rights or remedies determine the Subcontractor's employment under this Subcontract if the Subcontractor:

1. fails forthwith upon notice from the Contractor to commence remedial work to any defective workmanship and/or materials or fails to proceed with the same with due diligence or to complete such remedial work to the satisfaction of the Contractor or the Architect/Supervising Officer within a set period as the Contractor may specify in the said notice or if none is so specified within a reasonable time.

2. fails to withdraw immediately, at the request of the Contractor, any one or more of his employees to whom the Contractor objects or whose presence on the Works may contravene the conditions of this or the Principal Contract, or may cause labour disputes in the Subcontractor's or any other trade, and to replace such employees within a reasonable time by others against whom there is no such objection.

3. makes any arrangements with his creditors, has a Receiving Order made against him, executes a Bill of Sale, or commits an act of bankruptcy or, being a limited company, goes into liquidation, or has a Receiver appointed.

4. fails within seven days' notice in writing from the Contractor to comply with any of the obligations on the part of the Subcontractor herein contained.

Upon determination by the Contractor the Subcontractor shall not remove any of his equipment, materials or property from the Site and, notwithstanding anything contained in these conditions, shall be entitled to no further payment until completion of the Works by the Contractor or by others whereupon the Subcontractor shall become entitled to payment for Works executed and materials provided by the Subcontractor subject always to the right of the Contractor to set off all losses, expense and damages suffered or which may be suffered by the Contractor by reason of such determination and subject further to any other right of set off which the Contractor may have. For the purposes of such completion the Contractor shall have the right to use the Subcontractor's equipment, materials and property on the Site and to any materials or fabricated work lying at the Subcontractor's works or workshop which have been bought or fabricated for the purpose of this Subcontract.

7.2 Determination by the Subcontractor
The Subcontractor may without prejudice to any other of his rights or remedies determine the Subcontractor's employment under this Subcontract if the Contractor:

1. fails to make any progress payments within 14 days of it becoming due
2. unreasonably attempts or obstructs the carrying out of the Subcontractor's Works
3. makes any arrangements with his creditors, has a Receiving Order made against him, executes a Bill of Sale, or commits an act of bankruptcy or, being a limited company, goes into liquidation, or has a Receiver appointed.

Upon determination by the Subcontractor the Contractor shall pay to the Subcontractor, after taking into account amounts previously paid, such sum as shall be fair and reasonable for the value of work begun and executed, materials on site and the removal of all temporary buildings, plant tools and equipment. Provided always that the right of determination shall be without prejudice to any other rights or remedies which the Subcontractor may possess.

8.0 TEMPORARY WORKS AND SERVICES, ATTENDANCE, RELATED WORKS

8.1 Temporary accommodation
The Subcontractor shall provide to the approval of the Contractor and at his own expense, any requisite temporary site office, workshop accommodation, together with the necessary equipment, lighting, power, fuel, etc.

8.2 Welfare facilities
The Subcontractor shall, at his own risk have reasonable and free use of the temporary welfare accommodation and/or services (including First Aid facilities and treatment) which the Contractor or the Employer may provide on the Site in connection with the Works.

8.3 Temporary services
The Subcontractor shall, at his own risk, have reasonable and free use, in common with others engaged upon the Site, of the water supply, temporary plumbing, temporary lighting and temporary electric power. Electric power supply for small tools and equipment used on the Site shall not exceed 110v. A.C. single phase. Any electrical equipment used to carry out the Works must be in good mechanical condition and suitable for the electric power supply and fittings made available and fitted with suitable plugs, sockets and connectors to BS4343 (CEE 17) or any other standard that the Contractor may direct.

8.4 Use of scaffolding
The Subcontractor shall at his own risk and at such time(s) and for such period(s) as the Contractor may direct have free use of the Contractor's scaffolding, ladders and mechanical hoisting facilities which may be available on the Site or already in position.

8.5 Delivery and storage of materials
The Subcontractor shall provide all materials, package and carriage to and from the Site. He will be responsible for unloading during the progress of his Works, storing in the areas provided and moving his own materials at the Site. Any materials delivered prior to commencement on Site shall be off-loaded by the Contractor at the sole risk and cost of the Subcontractor.

8.6 Removal of rubbish etc.
All rubbish and/or surplus materials and plant of the Subcontractor must be removed forthwith from the vicinity of the Works, paths, roads etc., to an approved position on the Site.

8.7 Cutting away

In no circumstances whatsoever shall any cutting away be done without the prior written authority of the Contractor.

8.8 Sub-surfaces

The Subcontractor shall satisfy himself before commencing work, as to the suitability of any surfaces to which the Subcontractor is to fix, apply or lay his work.

Appendix C

Conditions of Contract for Building Works of a Jobbing Character (JA/C 90)

The Conditions

1·0   Intentions of the parties

Contract Documents – inconsistencies

1·1   The Contract Documents are

either

the accepted Tender and Agreement
('Agreement'), Annex A thereto and any
documents referred to therein and these
Conditions

or

the Works Order and any documents attached
thereto and these Conditions.

If there is any inconsistency between the
Conditions and the other Contract documents the
Conditions shall prevail.

The Contractor's obligation

1·2   The Contractor shall with due diligence and in a
good and workmanlike manner carry out and
complete the Works in accordance with the
Contract Documents and shall reasonably satisfy
the Employer that he has fulfilled this obligation.

The Employer's duties

1·3   The Employer shall issue in writing any further
information necessary for the proper carrying out
of the Works by the completion date given in the
Agreement/the Works Order and forthwith confirm
in writing any instruction given orally.

2·0   Commencement and Completion

Commencement and completion

2·1   The Works may be commenced on, and shall be
completed by, the dates given in the
Agreement/the Works Order.

Should the Contractor be delayed by the Employer
or for any reason beyond the Contractor's control,
the Employer shall fix a fair and reasonable revised
date for completion.

Defects liability

2·2   Any defects, excessive shrinkages or other faults
which appear within 6 weeks of completion of the
Works (or such other period stated in the
Agreement/the Works Order) and are due to

materials and/or workmanship not in accordance
with the Contract or to frost occurring before
completion shall be made good by the Contractor
at no cost to the Employer.

3·0   Control of the Works

Employer's instructions

3·1   The Employer may issue reasonable written
instructions which the Contractor shall forthwith
carry out.

Variations

3·2   The Employer may, without invalidating the
contract, instruct an addition to or omission from or
other change in the Works or the order or period in
which they are to be carried out subject to a right of
reasonable objection by the Contractor.
Compliance with any such instruction shall be
valued by agreement between the parties, failing
which it shall be valued by the Employer on a fair
and reasonable basis. Account shall be taken in
such valuation of any direct loss and/or expense
incurred by the Contractor due to the regular
progress of the Works being affected by
compliance with such instruction.

4·0   Payment

[a]   Invoice

4·1   Upon the completion of the Works in accordance
with the obligation in clause 1·2 the Contractor shall
submit to the Employer his invoice for discharge in
accordance with the terms of the Contract, which
shall include any amounts valued under clause 3·2
and any Value Added Tax on the amount invoiced.
Upon receipt of the invoice the Employer shall
check the invoice and consult the Contractor with
regard to the invoice or any part of its contents to
the extent that he is not satisfied therewith. Within
28 days of the receipt of the invoice the Employer,
having consulted the Contractor (if necessary),
shall endorse, by signature and date, and pass for
discharge the invoice as agreed by the Employer.

---

[a]   Payments on account for work executed, in cases where
the Contract period is extended beyond one month under
clause 2·1, should be made by agreement between the
Employer and the Contractor; if so made the invoice must
make allowance for any such payments made.

Payment due

4·2 After 14 days of the date so endorsed on the invoice and subject to the making good of any defects, excessive shrinkages or other faults that may by then have appeared and are due to materials and/or workmanship not in accordance with the Contract the agreed sum shall be a debt payable by the Employer to the Contractor.

5·0 Statutory obligations

Value Added Tax

5·1 The Employer shall be liable to pay to the Contractor such Value Added Tax as may be properly chargeable on the Contractor in respect of the supply to the Employer of the Works except to the extent that any such Value Added Tax or penalties related thereto are so chargeable because of some breach by the Contractor of the relevant statutory provisions.

Statutory tax deduction scheme

5·2 Where at the date of tender the Employer was a 'contractor', or where at any time up to and including the date when the Employer discharges the debt to which clause 4·2 refers the Employer becomes a 'contractor', for the purposes of the statutory tax deduction scheme established by the Finance (No.2) Act 1975 the Employer shall comply

[b] with the requirements thereof.

6·0 Prevention of corruption

Cancellation

6·1 The Employer shall be entitled to cancel this or any other contract and to recover from the Contractor the amount of any loss resulting from such cancellation, if the Contractor shall have offered or given or agreed to give to any person any gift or consideration of any kind or if the Contractor shall have committed any offence under the Prevention of Corruption Acts 1889 to 1916 or, where the Employer is a local authority, shall have given any fee or reward the receipt of which is an offence under sub-section (2) of section 117 of the Local Government Act 1972 or any amendment or re-enactment thereof.

7·0 Injury to persons and property – indemnity to Employer – insurance

Liability of Contractor – personal injury or death – indemnity to Employer

7·1·1 The Contractor shall be liable for, and shall indemnify the Employer against, any expense, liability, loss, claim or proceedings whatsoever arising under any statute or at common law in respect of personal injury to or the death of any person whomsoever arising out of or in the course of or caused by the carrying out of the Works, except to the extent that the same is due to any act or neglect of the Employer or of any person for whom the Employer is responsible.

Liability of Contractor – injury or damage to property – indemnity to Employer

7·1·2 The Contractor shall, subject to clause 7·2·1, be liable for, and shall indemnify the Employer against, any expense, liability, loss, claim or proceedings in respect of any injury or damage whatsoever to any property real or personal (other than the Works and all unfixed materials and goods intended for, delivered to or placed on or adjacent to the Works) insofar as such injury or damage arises out of or in the course of or by reason of the carrying out of the Works and to the extent that the same is due to any negligence, breach of statutory duty, omission or default of the Contractor or of any person employed or engaged by the Contractor upon or in connection with the Works.

Insurance against injury to persons or property

7·1·3 Without prejudice to the indemnity given to the Employer under clauses 7·1·1 and 7·1·2 the Contractor shall take out and maintain insurance in respect of claims arising out of his liability referred to in clauses 7·1·1 and 7·1·2:
- the insurance in respect of claims for personal injury to, or the death of, any person under a contract of service or apprenticeship with the Contractor, and arising out of and in the course of such person's employment, shall comply with the Employers' Liability (Compulsory Insurance) Act 1969 and any statutory orders made thereunder or any amendment or re-enactment thereof;
- for all other claims the insurance cover shall be not less than the amount stated in the Agreement/the Works Order for any one occurrence or series of occurrences arising out of one event.

[b] The application of the Statutory Tax Deduction Scheme is explained in the Inland Revenue booklet 'Construction Industry Tax Deduction Scheme' IR 14/15 1982: see also the JCT Practice Note 8.

Insurance of the Existing Structures and the Works – fire etc. – loss or damage

7·2·1　Before the Works are commenced the Employer
[c]　　shall:

　　·1　insure the existing structures together with the
　　　　contents thereof owned by him or for which he
　　　　is responsible for the full cost of reinstatement
　　　　against loss or damage by fire, lightning,
　　　　explosion, storm, tempest, flood, bursting or
　　　　overflowing of water tanks, apparatus or pipes,
　　　　earthquake, aircraft and other aerial devices or
　　　　articles dropped therefrom, riot and civil
　　　　commotion, and

　　·2　notify the insurers of his intention to have the
　　　　Works carried out, and

　　·3　require the insurance to include the Works
　　　　together with all unfixed materials and goods
　　　　intended for, delivered to or placed on or
　　　　adjacent to the Works for their full reinstatement
　　　　value against loss or damage by the perils listed
　　　　in clause 7·2·1·1, and

　　·4　have the interest of the Contractor as a joint
　　　　insured with the Employer recorded in the
　　　　relevant policy or any rights of subrogation
　　　　against the Contractor waived.

7·2·2　If any loss or damage to the Works and/or unfixed
　　　　materials or goods as referred to in clause 7·2·1
　　　　occurs then the Employer must issue instructions
　　　　for the reinstatement and making good of such loss
　　　　or damage or otherwise in accordance with clause
　　　　3·1 hereof and compliance with such instructions
　　　　shall be valued under clause 3·2.

Evidence of insurance

7·3　　The Contractor shall produce such evidence as the
　　　　Employer may reasonably require that the
　　　　insurances referred to in clause 7·1·3 have been
　　　　taken out and are in force at all material times.
　　　　Except where the Employer is a local authority, the
　　　　Employer shall produce such evidence as the
　　　　Contractor may reasonably require that the
　　　　obligations referred to in clause 7·2·1 have been
　　　　discharged and are being discharged at all material
　　　　times.

8·0　**Settlement of disputes – Arbitration**
[d]

Arbitration

8·1　　If any dispute or difference as to the construction of
　　　　this Contract or any matter or thing of whatsoever
　　　　nature arising thereunder or in connection
　　　　therewith shall arise between the Employer and the
　　　　Contractor, such dispute or difference shall be and
　　　　is hereby referred to the arbitration and final
　　　　decision of a person to be agreed between the
　　　　parties, or, failing agreement, within 14 days after
　　　　either party has given to the other a written request
　　　　to concur in the appointment of an Arbitrator, a
　　　　person to be appointed on the request of either
　　　　party by the President or a Vice-President for the
　　　　time being of the Royal Institution of Chartered
　　　　Surveyors.

Award

8·2　　The award of such Arbitrator shall be final and
　　　　binding on the parties.

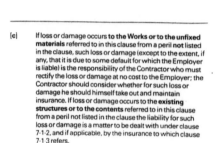

---

[c]　　If loss or damage occurs **to the Works or to the unfixed
　　　material** referred to in this clause from a peril **not** listed
　　　in the clause, such loss or damage (except to the extent, if
　　　any, that it is due to some default for which the Employer
　　　is liable) is the responsibility of the Contractor who must
　　　rectify the loss or damage at no cost to the Employer; the
　　　Contractor should consider whether for such loss or
　　　damage he should himself take out and maintain
　　　insurance. If loss or damage occurs to the **existing
　　　structures or to the contents** referred to in this clause
　　　from a peril not listed in the clause the liability for such
　　　loss or damage is a matter to be dealt with under clause
　　　7·1·2, and if applicable, by the insurance to which clause
　　　7·1·3 refers.

[d]　　The 'JCT' Arbitration Rules' dated 18 July 1988, may be
　　　used for the conduct of any arbitration if the parties so
　　　agree.

Table of Cases

Note: The following abbreviations of reports are used:

AC   – Law Reports Appeal Case Series
All ER – All England Law Reports
BLR   – Building Law Reports
Ch   – Law Reports Chancery Series
CILL   – Construction Industry Law Letter
CLD   – Construction Law Digest
KB   – Law Reports King's Bench Series
QB   – Law Reports Queen's Bench Series
STC   – Simon's Tax Cases
WLR   – Weekly Law Reports

Index

correction of errors and
  inconsistencies, 123, 137
correction of work improperly
  executed, 52
defects liability, 32–4
duties, 24–5, 105, 117
error of judgment, 58
exclusion of persons from the works,
  39
extension of contract period, 27–9, 137
final certificate, 57–8, 150
finality of certificates, 58–9
impartiality, 58
instructions, 40–41, 120–21, 139, 147
  following failure of work, 140
interim certificates, 51–2, 150
  unfixed materials, 54–5
levels and setting out, 139
naming of, 12–13
negligence, 12–13, 54
over-certification, 59
penultimate certificates, 56–7
postponement of work, 140
provisional sums, 139
removal of work, 140
replacement, 18–19
selection of specialist sub-contractors,
  44–7, 149
variation in works, 41–3, 139, 149
Architects and Surveyors Institute, *see*
  ASI
Architects (Registration) Acts 1931–64,
  13
articles of agreement
  ACA Form, 116
  ASI Small Works Contract, 147
  GC/Works/2, 104
  MW 80
    arbitration, 19
    replacement of architect, 18–19
    sum payable, 18
ASI (Architects and Surveyors Institute),
  146
  choosing the appropriate form, 160
ASI Minor Works Contract, 152
  commencement and completion, 153
  control of the works, 153–4
  determination, 155
  insurance, 154–5
  intentions of the parties, 153
  payment to the contractor, 154
  statutory obligations, 154
ASI Small Works Contract, 146–7

claims, 152
commencement and completion, 148
control of works, 148–9
determination, 151–2
discrepancies, 151
insurance, 151
intentions of the parties and
  contractor's obligations, 147–8
interim, final certificates and
  payments, 150
recitals and articles, 147
statutory obligations, 151
assignment, 35–6, 106–7, 119, 121–2
Atomic Energy Act 1946, 112

Barkey, J., 7
BEC (Building Employers
  Confederation), 5
BEC Guarantee Scheme for Small
  Building Works, 17
bills of quantities, *see* quantities
breach of contract
  architect's liability, 12
  contracts under seal, 20
  date of commencement 26
breach of statutory duty, 20
British Standards, 149
building contracts
  advantages of standard forms, 1–3
  ambiguities in, 2
  articles, *see* articles of agreement
  choice of, *see* choosing a form
  commencement, *see* commencement
  completion, *see* completion
  control of works, *see* control of works
  determination, *see* determination
  entered under hand or seal, 19–20
  exchange of letters, 1
  fixed price, 60, 124
  intentions of the parties, *see* intentions
    of the parties
  oral, 1
  payment, *see* payment
  range of forms, 3, 4
  recitals, *see* recitals
  repudiation, 95
  signature of the parties, 16, 19
  unfair terms, 2, 62
Building Employers Confederation, *see*
  BEC
Building (Prescribed Fees) Regulations
  1982, 62
Building Regulations 1985, 62

Index

Index